The World
of the
Rain Forest

Books by Robert Silverberg

Robert Silverberg

The World
of the
Rain Forest

Meredith Press
New York

First edition

Quotations on pages 88, 89, 103, 104, 108, 110, and 116 are
from *Book of Great Jungles* by Ivan Sanderson, copyright
1965 by Simon and Schuster, Inc. Reprinted by permission
of Simon and Schuster, Publishers.

Pictures on pages 8, 44, 81, 84, 88, 93, 96, 101, 102, 104,
107, 136, and 151 courtesy of the American Museum of
Natural History; pictures on pages 90, 111, and 113 courtesy
of New York Zoological Society.

Library of Congress Catalog Card Number: 67-14750

Manufactured in the United States
of America for Meredith Press

VAN REES PRESS   •   NEW YORK

Contents

1

Rain Forests of the World

This is the world of the rain forest: a silent world, a warm world, a green world, a wet world. Nothing changes here. The rain forest looked this way a million years ago. If man's bulldozers do not destroy it, it will look the same a million years from now.

Overhead, we cannot see the sky. There is only a canopy of leafy branches, more than a hundred feet above our heads. The branches interlock, forming an unbroken roof. Here and there a yellow beam of sunlight comes slanting through, but such invaders are rare. The rain forest is a dark place. A deep green color covers everything. We could almost be at the bottom of the sea.

Below the giant trees that make up the forest canopy, we see a level of smaller ones. Like the big trees, these have straight trunks, slender and tall, and there are no branches until the very top. In the rain forest the trees grow upward toward the dim light, rising swiftly and unbranchingly. There is little light at the best of times, and a tree must have light to grow. The tall trees of the high canopy receive plenty of light from above; the smaller trees living in their shade never get enough.

Down on the forest floor, there is hardly any light at all. Here, low plants struggle for life. They are widely spaced. In places, patches of bare earth can be seen. Down here, the rain forest seems like an open place. It is easy to walk about. We pass between the slim columns of the giant trees without difficulty.

The tropical rain forest is usually called a jungle. We think of explorers hacking their way through a jungle, slashing at the tangled vines and the thorny thickets. Some jungles are like that, but not the true rain forest. Because so little sunlight reaches the rain forest's floor, the thickets do not develop. There are tangled vines, all right, but they cling to the high trees. The undergrowth is never very dense.

Everything is green and glistening. The trees of a rain forest are mostly evergreens, so we never see brown autumn leaves here. The trees are not needly evergreens like our pines and spruces, but broad-leaved evergreens like our laurels and rhododendrons. Nearly all of them have long oval leaves, thick and leathery and dark green in color, with smooth edges. At first glance it may seem that the trees of the rain forest are all alike. Leaves, trunks, branches, all follow the same design. But actually the resemblance is just superficial. Nowhere else in the world can so many different types of trees be found in the same place.

The greenness is rarely broken by the gaiety of flowers. Rain-forest trees and plants have magnificent flowers in every color of the rainbow, but the flowers appear in the high branches, far above our heads. We on the forest floor are rarely aware of them. Nor do we see the bright-colored birds of the forest canopy. We see few animals, though there are many here. Forest animals learn how to stay hidden. All we see is the green world of the trees.

It may look monotonous. Green, green, green everywhere—
deep green that is almost black in the darkest places, a yellow-
green where the rays of the sun steal through the canopy, and
otherwise an unchanging dark green. Even the bark of the trees
looks greenish. The eye is dazzled by so much greenness. It is
hard to get accustomed to the look of the rain forest. At first
glance it looks endless and bewildering, a strange tangle of
shiny greenery.

The silence adds to the strange mood. The wind may blow,
but no breeze breaks through the canopy of leaves to ruffle the
branches below. Occasionally a bird may squawk far away, or
a monkey may laugh as it swings through the treetops, but
usually the creatures of the rain forest are silent. The only
sounds are small ones—the gurgling of a stream, the patter of
raindrops on leaves.

General rain forest view

It rains quite often. Sometimes the rain comes in terrible downpours, as though a waterfall were descending on the forest. More often, it comes in sudden drizzles. For fifteen minutes or so the rain trickles down like a thick mist. Then it stops for a while, and begins again. There may be a dozen or more such rainfalls a day. Almost never will there be a day with no rain at all. In a true tropical rain forest, the trees and plants need and get an amazing amount of rain.

It is always warm here, too, although cooler than it is just outside the forest. A muggy humid heat hangs over everything. The temperature rarely varies. Most of the time it is between 75° and 85°. The rain forest never gets as hot as New York City on a July afternoon, nor does it ever get as chilly as a Florida morning in October. There are no sudden cold snaps here. Month in and month out, the temperature remains in the same narrow range. There are no real seasons in a tropical rain forest. Some months are wetter than other months, but that is the only seasonal change.

A timeless world, then—seasonless, all of the same color, noiseless, damp, and without motion. At a first look, a rain forest seems bursting with life, trees and foliage everywhere. At a second look, it may seem an empty, forbidding place, dark and deserted, with nothing around but the lofty treetops.

The first look would be more accurate. A close examination shows what a busy place the rain forest really is. It is a community with many members.

In the earth live earthworms, ants, termites, bacteria, fungi— billions upon billions of creatures, each busy with a task necessary to the forest's life. On the surface of the forest floor live mosses and ferns, more fungi, and the insects that feed on decaying leaves and twigs. Small animals live here too, though we would have to look a long time to see them.

The middle level of the forest is the zone of the shrubs and the small trees. Here, in the comfortable wet warmth of the rain forest, the relatives of our small northern flowers grow to giant size. Daisies, violets, and other plants are trees here. Ferns, too, have woody trunks and stand fifteen to twenty feet tall. There is even a giant form of grass—bamboo.

These are the small trees. Above them rise the big ones, straight as arrows, often more than two hundred feet high. Many of them are enveloped in vines that wind around their trunks from floor to canopy. Others are decked out with dozens of sharp-leaved plants that prefer to grow high in the air, instead of on the ground. Great loops and coils of vine dangle down from the canopy. And up there, far above the forest floor, is a crowded world of life—bees and butterflies, birds, monkeys, squirrels, lizards. We are scarcely aware of them. Whole platoons of monkeys can go leaping through the thick foliage of the canopy without being visible from below.

We, standing on the forest floor, see little of the life of the forest unless we know where and how to look for it. We see only the towering trunks and the many shades of green. Standing there in the mist and drizzle and humidity, we may wonder why so many explorers and scientists have come under the magic spell of the rain forest.

That spell is real. A true rain forest is a majestic, awesome place. The giant trees stand like the columned pillars of some mighty cathedral. In the dim light, everything takes on an eerie beauty. The silence of the forest, the absence of wind, the blanket of warmth over everything, all combine to create a strange calm.

Those who have visited rain forests write of them in tones of wonder. Perhaps the most vivid of these descriptions is the work of the British-born newspaperman and adventurer of the last century, Sir Henry Stanley, who is best known for his successful search for the lost missionary, David Livingstone. Sixteen years

later Stanley made a journey through the rain forest of central
Africa, writing of it in his famous book, *In Darkest Africa*.

It was a strenuous trip. Stanley entered the forest in June,
1887, and, he tells us, "until Dec. 5, for 160 days, we marched
through the forest, bush and jungle, without ever having seen a
bit of greensward of the size of a cottage chamber floor." Stanley's party suffered from starvation, fever, and the attacks of
unfriendly natives and unfriendlier insects. Misery and hunger
made the forest seem hateful. And yet, Stanley wrote:

"If once we absented ourselves from camp, and the voices of

Sir Henry Stanley

the men died away, and we forgot our miseries, and were not absorbed by the sense of the many inconveniences, an awe of the forest rushed upon the soul and filled the mind. The voice sounded with rolling echoes, as in a cathedral. One became conscious of . . . the absence of sunshine, its subdued light, and marveled at the queer feeling of loneliness, while inquiringly looking around to be assured that this loneliness was no delusion. It was as if one stood amid the inhabitants of another world."

About four hundred years before Stanley wrote that, an even more celebrated explorer was setting down his impressions of a tropical rain forest. He was Christopher Columbus, probably the first European to see and write about such a forest. In 1493, Columbus wrote this description of the island of Hispaniola in the West Indies:

"Its lands are high and there are in it very many sierras and very lofty mountains. . . . All are most beautiful, of a thousand shapes, and all are accessible and filled with trees of a thousand kinds and tall, and they seem to touch the sky. And I am told that they never lose their foliage, as I can understand, for I saw them as green and as lovely as they are in Spain in May and some of them were flowering, some bearing fruit, and some in another stage, according to their nature."

Other men have added their own views—such as those of the scientist Henry Walter Bates, who explored the forests of Brazil between 1848 and 1859. "There is something in a tropical forest akin to the ocean in its effect on the mind," Bates wrote. "Man feels so completely his insignificance there and the vastness of nature."

The rain forests of the world have been explored, measured, and studied. Their numerous types of plant and animal life have been listed in the scientific catalogs. We know how a rain forest comes into being and what conditions it must have to remain a rain forest.

All these things were mysteries a hundred years ago. The term "rain forest" itself was not coined until 1898. A German scientist, Andreas Franz Wilhelm Schimper, invented it to describe the tropical evergreen forest, otherwise known as "jungle," "bush," or "brush." Yet even now the rain forest holds many problems for science. There is a difference between knowing what happens in a rain forest and how it happens, and knowing *why* it happens. The "why" of the rain forest is still a puzzle in many respects.

What is a rain forest, exactly?

Andreas Schimper defined it very carefully. A rain forest, he said, consists of evergreen trees living in a warm, humid climate. The trees must be at least a hundred feet tall, though usually they are much taller, and the forest must be rich in thick-stemmed vines and in epiphytes, which are plants that grow on the branches of trees.

Such rain forests are found only in tropical lowlands. These are the *true* rain forests. However, tropical rain forests may also occur on the slopes of mountains, where rainfall and temperature conditions are right. These *submontane* and *montane* rain forests are similar to the lowland forests in many ways, but the size and distribution of the trees can be quite different.

Entirely in another category is the *temperate* rain forest. The only rain forest in the continental United States is of this type; it is located in Olympic National Park in the State of Washington. A temperate rain forest is found in cool but not cold regions that get an unusual amount of rain. The trees grow to great size, and the underbrush is exceptionally lush. However, the trees of such a forest are the typical northern ones, such as pines and spruces. None of the common tropical trees are found in a temperate rain forest. Nor does a temperate rain forest have the unique "canopy" structure of the tropical kind.

Finally, there is the tropical deciduous rain forest. Deciduous trees are trees that drop all their leaves at a certain season of the year. In northern countries, such trees as maples, oaks, and elms shut down for the winter, dropping their leaves when cold weather comes. In the tropics, there is never any cold weather, but sometimes there are long dry seasons. A true rain forest cannot develop where the rainfall is not steady and heavy all year around. In such places, a deciduous forest appears. During the rainy season it looks very much like any lowland rain forest. But when the dry weather comes, the trees shed their leaves. Though such forests are considered rain forests, this book will deal most of the time with the true or evergreen rain forest of the tropics.

There are two main conditions for the development of an evergreen tropical rain forest: temperature and rainfall.

Olympic rain forest, Washington

The temperature must be mild all year around. Tropical trees can be quickly killed by low temperatures. Rain forests develop only where the average temperature ranges from 70° to 80°. An average yearly temperature of about 64° is the lowest that rain-forest trees can tolerate.

Of course, if the temperature averages 105° for half the year and 35° for the other half, the yearly average is 70°. Clearly this would not do for a rain forest. There must not be any large fluctuation in temperature from one day to the next, or from one season to the next.

Only in the tropics is this condition found. In most parts of the world, the sun's rays strike the earth at different angles in different times of the year, producing variations in temperature. The weather is hot when the sunlight strikes from straight overhead, cool when it strikes at an angle. Along the equator, the sun is overhead twelve months a year, and the weather is always warm, with little variation. Near the equator, the average temperature of the hottest months may be no more than 10° higher than that of the coolest ones. In the north, with its hot summers and cold winters, the difference can be more than 100°.

So in the tropics the temperature is warm and even. However, warmth by itself is not enough for a rain forest. Some of the warmest places in the world are barren deserts. There must be adequate rainfall too.

An evergreen rain forest requires twelve months of heavy rain a year. The minimum yearly rainfall must be about 120 inches. Even a deciduous rain forest needs to get at least eighty inches of rain a year. That in itself is quite a good deal: more than two million gallons of water per acre. New York, by comparison, receives about forty inches of rain a year. Louisiana, one of the wettest states in the United States, gets about sixty-three inches a year.

Not only must the rainfall be heavy, it must be evenly dis-

tributed throughout the year. An evergreen rain forest must have
at least eight inches of rain a month, normally. In some places the
high humidity of the air allows a forest to get along with less
rain. A rain forest in Nigeria, for example, gets about ninety
inches a year, and has five straight months of less than four
inches. In three of these months the rainfall is below two inches.
Almost anywhere else, a rain forest could not exist under such
conditions. But the moisture in the air sustains the trees through
the dry months, and the heavy rainfall in the seven wet months
does the rest.

Most real rain forests get much more than the minimum quota
of rain. Annual rainfalls of two hundred to three hundred inches
are common. Rainfalls of four hundred inches or more are found
in some parts of the tropics. That is more than an inch of rain a
day. In contrast, most parts of the eastern United States average
about an inch of rain a week. West of the Mississippi there is less
rain than that. Los Angeles gets fourteen inches of rain a year,
less than some rain forests receive in two weeks. Phoenix, Arizona, averages only seven inches of rain a year.

In the area along the equator, it rains practically every day. A
rain forest in Africa's Cameroons averages 194 rainy days a
year; one in Guyana, South America, records 212 rainy days a
year. On the islands of Martinique and Dominica, in the West
Indies, rain falls about three hundred days a year in the mountainous rain forests. These rainfalls usually take the form of
light, frequent showers, though occasionally there are fierce
downpours. The equatorial regions have no real dry season. What
the local people call the dry season is simply less wet than the
wet season. In the wet season it may rain an inch or so every day
for months; in the "dry" season, the rainfall may arrive at the
rate of two or three inches a week. That is still more than enough
to support a lush rain forest.

The combination of warmth and heavy rainfall in the tropics

is no coincidence. Rain occurs when warm, moisture-laden air
rises to meet cold air in the upper atmosphere. The collision of
warm air and cold air causes water vapor to condense into drops
and fall as rain.

The air is always moist in the tropics because about three
fourths of the tropical zone is covered by ocean. The heat of the
sun causes ocean water to evaporate and become vapor carried
by the air. At the same time, the sun's warmth causes this moist
tropical air to rise, since warm air always rises. When it meets
the cool air high overhead, rain is produced.

The process goes on all the time: water evaporating from the
sea, the moist air rising, the rain coming down. In the heat of
the day, the air over the land is warmer than the air over the
ocean, and so cool, wet ocean air is constantly being pulled land-
ward to replace the warm air over the land that has risen. Thus
there is a belt of humid, high-rainfall territory that follows the
equator. This is the zone of the true rain forest. By following the
line of the equator around the world, we can see where the rain
forests are.

In the Western Hemisphere, the equator passes through the
upper part of South America. Ecuador, Colombia, and Brazil are
right on the equator. Venezuela, Guyana, Surinam, and French
Guiana are close to it. All of these countries have rain forests.
The South American rain forest is the greatest in the world.

There is no rain forest along the western coast of South America, except in one small area. Cold ocean currents sweeping up
from Antarctica keep the air cool and free from moisture, so that
there is never any rainfall. The coast of Peru is one of the driest
deserts in the world. Only in northwestern South America—the
coasts of Ecuador and Colombia—do warm, moist Pacific winds
bring enough rainfall to allow rich forests to grow.

The mountain chain know as the Andes runs a short distance

inland from South America's western coast. East of the Andes the land is low and moist. Here, spreading across the entire upper half of the continent to the Atlantic shore, is the lushest of all rain forests. Two mighty rivers flow through the jungle country: the Orinoco and the Amazon.

The giant rain forest lies both north and south of the Amazon. It reaches as far south as the borders of Bolivia and Paraguay, as far north as northern Venezuela. For thousands of miles the green canopy stretches, broken here and there by the courses of huge rivers. But the rain forest of the Amazon basin is not continuous. In some areas the forest thins out and gives way to low shrubbery. In other places, the rain forest is replaced by the flat, rolling grassland known as a savanna. The rain forest cannot grow in these regions because the soil is too sandy or too shallow. And in eastern Brazil, the rainfall is not heavy enough to support an evergreen rain forest, so a deciduous forest has appeared instead. On the east coast of Brazil, beyond this deciduous zone, is a separate rain forest cut off from the main jungle.

Following the equator eastward across the Atlantic, we see that it runs through the middle of Africa. It passes through Gabon, the Congo Republic, the Republic of the Congo (a different nation), Uganda, Kenya, and Somalia. The rain-forest zone extends across all these countries. In the west, the rain-forest zone runs along the coast as far north as Nigeria, Ghana, Liberia, and Guinea. In the east it reaches down through Tanzania as far as Lake Tanganyika.

The African rain forest is interrupted in many places. There are regions where the natives have completely destroyed it by farming, and other regions where low rainfall does not permit rain-forest development. Thus a great deal of Ghana and Nigeria has no rain forest. In eastern Africa, much of the country is mountainous, and so there can be no true rain forest. There are large areas of savanna throughout equatorial Africa. Such animals as lions and giraffes, mistakenly thought to be "jungle" beasts, are found only in these savannas, never in the rain forests.

Eastward from Africa the line of the equator passes through the Indian Ocean, the islands of Indonesia, and Borneo. Then it crosses the Pacific, going just north of New Guinea and cutting over the numerous small island groups of the ocean. In this part of the world, the best rain forests are found not directly on the equator but a little to the north and south of it. Ceylon, western India, Thailand, and the Philippines all have tropical rain forests. So do Vietnam, Cambodia, and Laos, and the other countries of that peninsula. Sumatra, Borneo, and New Guinea have large rain forests, as does a narrow strip of Australia's eastern coast. Some islands of the western Pacific, such as Fiji, Samoa, and the New Hebrides, also belong in the rain-forest zone.

When we go north or south from the equator, the rainfall patterns change. Though it is nearly as warm, local climate conditions tend to produce one or more dry seasons a year. The lands 10° south of the equator have a long dry season from April to September, and a short dry season in December and January. The lands 10° north of the equator have their long dry season from October to March, and their short dry season in June and July. In these places, the climate is warm enough to support a rain forest, but severe dry spells often make rain-forest growth impossible. Only if there is an ample supply of water in the ground and in the air can the rain-forest trees survive such droughts.

The existence of rain forests away from the equator, then, depends on a cluster of local conditions. In the months when the sun is not directly overhead, rainfall tends to drop off. Certain ocean currents also affect rainfall. In Asia, the climate pattern permits rain forests to grow as far north of the equator as southern China. In North America, the same latitude is desert country in Mexico. In Africa, the land lying more than 10° north of the equator is also too dry, generally, for rain forests.

Sometimes *gallery* forests or *fringing* forests develop in warm regions where the weather is too dry for real rain-forest growth. These are tropical forests that stand along the banks of rivers. A short distance in from the rivers, open grasslands are found. Many early explorers, traveling by river and seeing gallery forests, made the mistake of thinking that they were passing through extensive rain forests continuing far inland. In that way the jungles of the Congo and the Amazon were thought to be much greater in size than they actually are.

The absolute limits of tropical rain forest are the two imaginary lines known as the Tropics, which set the boundaries for the warm zone of the world. The Tropic of Cancer lies at $23\frac{1}{2}°$ north latitude, the Tropic of Capricorn at $23\frac{1}{2}°$ south latitude. Everything between them is tropical country.

In the Western Hemisphere, the northern limb of the rain-forest zone runs right up to the Tropic of Cancer. This forest zone covers most of Central America and the eastern coastal district of Mexico. It also includes many of the islands of the West Indies. Such islands as Dominica, Trinidad, Martinique, and Jamaica have areas of rain forest. So does Puerto Rico. Puerto Rico's Caribbean National Forest gets 180 inches of rain a year. However, the West Indian rain forests are generally of the montane variety, rather than of the lowland type. Puerto Rico's forest is three thousand feet high on a mountain known as El Yunque.

A narrow strip of the Amazon rain forest actually reaches south of the Tropic of Capricorn for a short distance. Australia's rain forest also goes south of the boundary. In Burma, the upper part of the rain forest is north of the Tropic of Cancer. Everywhere else, though, true rain forests are found only in the $47°$-wide strip between the two Tropics. In Africa the rain-forest belt is much narrower—from $10°$ north to $10°$ south.

The rain forests lying beyond the tropical zone are quite different. In New Zealand, southeastern Australia, southern Chile, and several other parts of the world, local rainfall conditions are such that extremely lush forests are produced. The trees are evergreen and extraordinarily tall, and there is a rich accompanying flora of vines and shrubbery. But the weather is too cool for tropical trees, and the forests are composed of species entirely different from those in tropical rain forests.

One of the most spectacular of these temperate rain forests is in the United States—the forest of the Olympic National Park, Washington. Here, moist winds coming in from the Pacific are unable to carry their burden of moisture over the towering Olympic Mountains. They drop their rain on the strip of forest west of the mountains, delivering 150 to 200 inches a year. The land east of these mountains is almost as dry as a desert. In the mild wet climate of the temperate rain forest, some trees become giants more than two hundred feet high.

The rain forest, whether temperate or tropical, lowland or montane, is a place of strangely moving beauty. Though rain forests are made up of different species of trees in different parts of the world, the effect they produce is always the same. Henry Stanley told how "an awe of the forest rushed upon the soul and filled the mind." The mood is the same, whether in Malaya or Brazil or the depths of the Congo. We do not know why the silent forest stirs such awe within us. Men have made lists of the forest's trees, and have given every shrub and bug a long Latin name. They have captured the brilliantly hued butterflies of the forest, and they have counted the number of bacteria in a cubic inch of the forest's soil. They have devised elaborate explanations to tell us why the forest grows the way it does. The scientists have studied the rain forest in its every detail. But they cannot account for the chills that run down the spine as we stand beneath the lofty canopy of green.

Here stands the forest, millions of years old, a dark place of warmth and mystery. Here stand we, very small on the forest floor. We are among giants, and we are in a world that is not like our world. And we feel a strange unscientific thrill as we wander through that world.

2

Within the Rain Forest

From the outside, the rain forest looks like an impenetrable wall of green. Flying over the Amazon jungle in an airplane, we see what appears to be a fuzzy green carpet stretching in all directions. The crowns of the tallest trees, close together and bound to one another by vines, form an unbroken roof. Now and then, a taller tree sticks out above the others. Scientists call such trees *emergents*. Mainly, though, the forest from above presents a smooth and solid appearance.

If we take a river trip down the Congo or the Amazon, the forest looks just as solid. On each bank of the river rises a green barrier. Tall trees and short trees and shrubs are all tangled together, so knotted by twining vines that it seems impossible to pass between them. Many of the early explorers did not try to enter the forest. To them, it seemed pointless to attempt to hack a path into that dense, tight curtain of vegetation.

But the view that a rain forest displays along a river bank is an unnatural one. The river creates an opening in the forest, allowing tropical sunlight to come through. Wherever this sunlight touches the forest, growth increases vastly. Trees and vines put out new leaves that hungrily reach toward the light. An exaggerated lushness is the result.

Come inside the forest, and you will see that the interior is quite different. As we chop our way through the barrier, we step from a bright, hot world to a cool, dark one. The spreading canopies of the big trees choke off light from above, making it difficult for plants and shrubs to survive on the ground. Those that we see have leaves of a reddish or purplish tint. These pigments enable the leaves to make use of what little light strikes them.

There is surprisingly little underbrush. The ground is bare. It may be muddy from a recent rain, and as we walk along, our shoes get caught in the sticky stuff. We find it easier to take them off and go barefoot. The cool mud feels good against our skin.

There is no thick carpet of fallen leaves, as in a northern underbrush. Leaves fall here too, but almost at once they rot and

Interior of rain forest   Rain forest, streamside view

turn to soil. The ones we see fell in the last few days. Great logs and even fallen trees lie on the ground, sometimes blocking our way. When we touch them, we discover that they are as soft as soggy paper. They, too, are beginning to decay. There is a scent of mildew in the air.

The coolness is delightful. Outside, in the full blaze of the tropical sunlight, it was hot—90° or more. Under the closed canopy of the forest it is 15° or 20° cooler. The darkness and the moisture help to create that effect. Humid mists drift through the forest like low-lying clouds. There is no breeze in here. The weather is practically unchanging.

Only at the canopy level does the forest temperature fluctuate at all. In the morning, as the hot sun rises higher in the sky, the canopy grows warm. Little of this sunlight and warmth gets through the dense foliage to the forest floor, though. A sudden thunderstorm may drop the temperature of the canopy by several degrees in a few minutes; but the forest floor is protected from that change, too. And at night, when the canopy is giving off the heat it absorbed during the day, the forest floor does not grow much cooler.

Nearly everything in the rain forest, large or small, has a woody trunk. It is not surprising that the big trees have trunks, of course. But even the vines and shrubs and flowering plants are sturdy of stem. This is one of the special characteristics of rain-forest vegetation. Such northern flowering plants as milkworts, vervains, daisies, violets, and periwinkles become trees the size of oaks and maples.

Another special feature of the rain forest is the great variety of living things. A northern forest may consist of ten or fifteen species of big trees—often fewer—and a few dozen types of shrubs. Here, nature has been much more generous. A single acre of rain forest may hold a hundred kinds of large trees.

Scientists have estimated that three thousand species of trees are found in the rain forests of Indonesia, and at least twenty-five hundred species in the Amazon jungles. The island of Trinidad, just off the northeastern coast of South America, has 1,289 plant species, of which 364 are trees, in an area of 1,750 square miles.

This fantastic variety of vegetation makes life complicated for the scientist trying to study rain-forest botany. Not only is there a multitude of species, but many of them have the same general appearance, so it is difficult to identify the various types. Confronted with a row of identical-looking trunks, the botanist must find some way to get at the leaves. Binoculars are not always helpful. Some explorers have used rifles to shoot down branches for study; others have gone so far as to train monkeys to tear off leaves and bring them down. Alfred Russel Wallace, a great naturalist of the nineteenth century who explored rain forests both in Brazil and Malaya, described the problems of research under these conditions this way in 1878:

"If the traveler notices a particular species and wishes to find more like it, he may often turn his eyes in vain in every direction. Trees of varied forms, dimensions, and colors are around him, but he rarely sees any one of them repeated. Time after time he goes towards a tree which looks like the one he seeks, but a closer examination proves it to be distinct. He may at length, perhaps, meet with a second specimen half a mile off, or may fail altogether, till on another occasion he stumbles on one by accident."

The pattern of growth is the same for nearly all trees and shrubs. Everything grows straight up, toward the light. There is little point in putting out branches except at the summit of growth, for their leaves would get little light. Since leaves are the factories by which the members of the plant kingdom turn sunshine into energy, they must always turn toward the source of light. Sunlight pulls the forest upward. The trees are straight and slim, lacking the complex tracery of branches and twigs that trees of the temperate zone commonly have.

This hunger for light produces the rain forest's most unusual feature—the zoning into separate and distinct levels of growth.

At first glance this zoning may be hard to see. We may have the same problem as the man who couldn't see the forest because all the trees were in the way. In the rain forest, we discover that trees of every size are all over the place, growing in hopeless confusion and bound together by a wild webwork of climbing vines. Growth seems unrestrained and entirely incredible. Trees sprout from the trunks of other trees; air plants bedeck the boughs of the tall trees; shrubs sprawl in every direction. Except at ground level, there does not seem to be an open space.

But there is a pattern in the bewildering chaos. A careful look shows an arrangement of several tiers or stories of vegetation. Though it seems that everything from floor to canopy is densely packed with greenery, the growth of the rain forest is actually separated into five distinct layers. There are three levels of trees: big ones, medium-sized ones, and small ones. Below the smallest trees is a level of woody shrubs. The fifth level is that of the plants that grow on the forest floor.

Some degree of zoning can also be found in northern temperate forests, of course. The zoning there is usually into three levels; big trees, small trees, and ground plants. But only in the rain forest are the zoning boundaries drawn so sharply. The closed canopy at the roof of the rain forest creates very special conditions of life for the trees growing beneath it. Few temperate forests are so dense on top that the young trees are totally shut off from light. In the rain forest, though, life in the lower levels is an endless and difficult struggle to reach the energy-giving rays of the sun.

The arrangement of the zones depends on the tree population

of the rain forest. In some forests the tallest trees all belong to the same species. They generally grow to the same height and form a tightly closed canopy. Such forests, known as *single-dominant* rain forests, are found everywhere in the rain-forest zones of the world. Some of them extend for hundreds of miles. In a single-dominant forest, the zoning is extremely sharp. The canopy is continuous, looking from above like a green ocean, and there is an unusually clean division between the trees of the solid canopy and the small, struggling trees beneath.

One single-dominant forest is found in the lowlands of Trinidad. About 95 percent of the tall trees are of the species known as *Mora excelsa*. This tree, a giant relative of the string bean and the sweet pea, makes up a continuous canopy about 115 feet above the ground. Botanists call this the A level of the rain forest. Beneath it is a B level of trees ranging from thirty-six to seventy-five feet in height, and beneath that is a C level of trees from twelve to twenty-five feet tall. Of course, there are always some trees that do not quite fit into either lower level—those that are thirty or ninety feet tall and in the process of growing up to the next level—but in the main the lines of separation are very obvious.

Matters are more complicated in the rain forests where no one species of tree is dominant. Such forests, called *mixed* rain forests, are the most common kind. Here, the A level of big trees is made up of a number of different species. Each species reaches a different maximum height, and so the canopy of a mixed forest is bumpy and irregular. Most of the trees may be from 120 to 150 feet high, but some may stop growing at one hundred feet while others may shoot up two hundred feet or more. The result is a ragged, uneven canopy, and a good deal of sunlight may be able to enter the open places.

This allows the trees of the B level to grow taller than they could in a single-dominant rain forest. Some of them, in fact, may grow until they reach the lower limits of the A-level range. Thus the distinction between A-level (canopy) trees and B-level trees becomes blurred. In some mixed rain forests, the two levels join to form a single canopy. However, the C level far below remains clearly marked off from the upper levels, since it gets little light. It forms a canopy of its own, fifteen or twenty feet above the forest floor, making life difficult for the plants and shrubs still lower down.

The trees of the C level consist mostly of species that could never grow more than twenty-five feet tall, no matter how much sunshine they got. Also found in the C level are the young saplings of the B-level trees, and a very few saplings of A-level trees. The B level too has its permanent trees, limited in height to fifty or seventy-five feet under the best of conditions. Unlike the C-level trees, which are tightly bound together by vines and form a closed canopy, the trees of the B level are spaced far apart. Among them, of course, are young A-level trees that have not yet reached their full height.

The A-level trees are the giants of the rain forest. They grow at widely separated intervals, but since they reach the sunlight they are able to develop wide, heavy, umbrella-shaped crowns. These big crowns reach out until they touch, forming the closed canopy of the forest roof.

Each tree level is designed and adapted for its place in the rain forest. C-level trees can get along with little sunlight; they may die, rather than grow taller, if they receive more light than they are accustomed to getting. B-level trees require a greater deal of light, but they, too, are happiest when living in the half-light beneath the top canopy. The A-level trees thrive only when they are in the bright sunlight and open air above the canopy they create.

This causes some difficulties for young A-level trees as they grow their way up through the lower levels of the forest. Explaining the development of new A-level trees is one of the toughest problems scientists have dealt with in the rain forest.

It seems that the arrival of a new A-level tree is a rare event in the forest community. The tall trees send a steady shower of seeds to the forest floor, but the odds are heavy against any one of these seeds giving rise to a full-fledged forest titan.

In some rain forests, few of the seeds of A-level trees ever sprout. This is true in the evergreen forests of western Africa, where saplings of the A-level trees are so rare that the natives say these big trees "never have children." On the other hand, in the rain forests of Asia and South America, the seedlings of the tall trees form dense thickets of undergrowth. But most of these seedlings die from lack of light. Sometimes an entire crop of seedlings perishes before it is two years old.

Perhaps one out of a hundred, or even one out of a thousand, A-level seedlings survives to reach a height of ten or twenty feet. The lucky survivor must then face a long period of what botanists call *suppression*. Living in the dark C level, the young sapling grows extremely slowly. Decades may pass with scarcely any increase in height or girth. The tree is competing with all those around it for light, and its roots must fight for water in the crowded soil. Those A-level seedlings that get past the seedling stage usually have long lives, but they may spend endless years as stunted members of the C level of the forest.

The only chance they have to reach their full growth comes when a gap is created in the levels above. Perhaps a savage hurricane will rip across the forest canopy, tearing apart the crowns of the tall trees and allowing sunlight to reach the lower levels. Or perhaps one of the big trees will come to the end of its natural life span and topple to the ground. (No one knows how long an A-level rain forest lives. Many of the shorter trees die naturally in twenty-five years or less, but some of the giants are thought to be 250 years old and still healthy.)

When a gap is formed in the forest, there is sudden swift growth in the underbrush. The C-level trees that thrive in shade may die quickly as the sunlight reaches them. A few of the B-level trees may grow a little larger. But this is the time for some long-suppressed sapling of an A-level tree to come into its own. After years of waiting, it shoots up with amazing speed to fill the gap. Within a few years a new forest giant has taken its place high above.

On its way up through the levels, the growing tree has changed the shape of its crown several times to match its surroundings. Down on the C level, its crown was much taller than it was wide, with a pointed, cone-shaped outline. When it reached the B level, its crown widened slightly, but still was long and tapering. Finally, at the roof of the forest, its crown spreads, becoming wide and flat, adopting the typical umbrella shape of a forest tree with access to sunlight.

Thus the forest changes and yet remains the same. Individual trees die, but the three zones of trees keep their relative positions. At any time there is always a level of very large trees, a level of middle-sized trees, and a level of small trees. Generally there are wide gaps between each of these levels, broken only by the occasional trees that are growing into the next highest level.

It has been like this for millions of years. The rain forests of the world are known technically as *climax* forests. That is, they have reached their final form and will undergo no changes of a major sort. In other parts of the world, forests may be in a process of change; where the weather is gradually growing warmer, for example, forests of birch and maple may take the place of forests of pine and spruce. But in the rain-forest zone, all is as it has been since the days of the dinosaurs.

Today's rain forests, though, are isolated patches of what once was a world-wide jungle. A hundred million years ago, much of the earth was tropical in climate, and there were thick rain forests as far north as London and New York. The world's climate has changed, and the rain-forest zone has retreated toward the equator. Even a hundred years ago, a much larger part of the world was covered with rain forest than today. The activities of modern man have cut into the forest, destroying great strips of it so that towns and plantations might be founded. In much of Africa and to a lesser degree in South America, the virgin rain forest has been obliterated by civilization.

In the changeless world beneath the canopy of green, only the shifting seasons bring some variation in the rhythm of life. A temperate forest goes into a resting period when cold weather comes; the deciduous trees drop their leaves, the hardy evergreens become dormant. There is no "winter" in the tropics, of course—just the alternation of wet seasons and dry. Depending on how dry the dry season is, the forest will show the effects of the climatic change.

In the true lowland rain forests along the equator, there is no real dry season. Some months may bring less rain than others, but rain falls practically every day of the year. Here, the evergreen forest shows no seasonal variation. Each tree and plant has a resting period when it shifts to a slower gear, putting out fewer new leaves and flowers, but there is no fixed timetable for these resting periods. On the same tree, one branch may be resting, another in full flower, at the same time.

In the forests north and south of the equator, where definite patterns of wet and dry weather are common, the seasonal shifts are more pronounced. Many species will become inactive during the dry weather and will burst into new growth when the heavy rains return. Some may drop many leaves in dry times, to reduce the loss of water.

Even the evergreen trees must drop their leaves, though generally never all at once. A rain-forest evergreen usually produces new leaves in periodic bursts of growth, three or six or even twelve months apart. One tree may bear leaves of the last two or three growth periods at the same time. Eventually, the oldest leaves become yellow or red and fall off. Sometimes whole branches may be bare for a few days, though new leaves have appeared on other branches. A few "evergreen" trees of the forest actually lose all their leaves at once, sprouting new foliage in a week or so.

Deciduous trees, which may be bare for weeks or even months at a time, are most common in rain forests that suffer regular dry spells. However, they are also found even in climates of uniformly distributed heavy rainfall. Every evergreen tropical rain forest has some deciduous trees. These are almost always in the A level; B- and C-level trees are usually evergreen in lowland rain forests.

The rhythm of flowering is just as unpredictable as that of leaf growth. Most temperate species flower in the spring or early summer, though some shrubs flower in the fall. But in the rain forest, flowering continues all the year round. Some species blossom almost continuously. Others flower at regularly spaced intervals throughout the year. Each species follows its own schedule.

Where there is a dry season, it is customarily the time of greatest flowering. Perhaps the trees flower then so the new seeds will have the benefit of the rainy season that is to come. Andreas Schimper, the German scientist who studied rain forests at the turn of this century, found that on Java 63 percent of the species flowered in the dry season, 8 percent in the rainy season, and 29 percent at times unrelated to the weather. In Guyana, South America, the greatest amount of flowering took place at the beginning of the long dry season in September, and both at the beginning and end of the short dry season that lasts from February to April. On the other hand, in the rain forests of the New Hebrides islands, there is one main flowering season in the wettest part of the year, and another, not so great, in the time of lowest rainfall.

A special feature of rain-forest flowering is *gregarious* blossoming. All the individuals of the same species may suddenly burst into flower at the same time, over areas of many square miles. In the Amazon basin, for example, all the myrtles may produce fragrant white flowers the same day; in Malaya, all the coffee bushes of one species will flower together in the same district on the same day, those of other species flowering together on different days. Gregarious blossoming is usually related to the weather. Some sudden change in the weather is the signal for it to begin. A thundershower or severe storm following a dry spell may touch the phenomenon off. A rapid drop of several degrees in temperature can produce the effect also.

Though every plant and tree in the forest flowers regularly, the flowers do not always produce seeds. In the lush rain forest there is often no room for new growth, and the showy flowers prove to be sterile. This is particularly true among the A-level and B-level trees. Some of them flower two or three times a year, but produce fertile seeds only every third year. Others may flower at intervals of eighteen months or two years, producing fertile seeds each time.

The forest trees distribute their seeds in many ways. The tallest trees often have light winged seeds that are blown to other regions by the wind. The silk-cotton tree, or ceiba, produces tiny round seeds that nestle within a capsule packed with fine silky threads. The ripe capsule bursts, and the seeds float away on these fluffy threads. The seeds of the mahogany tree are thin and flat, and have delicate wings. When the seedpod bursts, the seeds are thrown into the air and carried away. Other A-level seeds have silky "parachutes" that carry them for miles.

Beneath the canopy, though, there is no breeze, and different methods of distribution are necessary. Some trees have huge heavy fruits or nuts that break loose and fall with a thump to the forest floor. If they remained there, the seedlings would die in the shade of the mother tree. But forest animals feed on the meat of the seedcases, swallowing the seeds and scattering them afterward in their droppings. Forest elephants and wild pigs may gulp these big fruits whole, later planting the seeds miles away.

Other trees depend on the cooperation of the birds and monkeys that live in the treetops. They produce juicy little fruits or nuts that are eaten and excreted in some other part of the forest. The seeds of some of the small plants that grow in the treetops

Cannonball tree, illustrating cauliflory

are sticky, and cling to the beaks of birds which feed on them. They are later scraped off on the branches of other trees, where they sprout and live far above the ground.

One of the many special features of rain-forest trees is *cauli-flory:* the sprouting of flowers directly from the trunk or the main branches. In most northern trees, flowers and seeds are always borne on small twigs. Some rain-forest trees can produce flower buds anywhere along their trunk or branches. An example is the cacao tree, from whose seeds chocolate is made. The large rough pods of this tree cling to the sides of its trunk like strange growths.

Cauliflory is quite common in the rain forest, though it is extremely rare elsewhere. About a thousand cauliflorous species are known, most of them tall shrubs or small trees of the C level. Scientists have offered many theories for this curious habit, but none has won general acceptance. One of the first and most logical ideas was put forth by Alfred Russel Wallace in 1878. He suggested that cauliflory helped the smaller trees of the forest display their flowers where they could most easily be reached by butterflies and other insects that fertilized them. The C level is the most dense in the forest, and flowers carried in the usual place on the branches might be less easily noticed than those on the trunk.

Another suggestion, offered in 1926 by a botanist named Haberlandt, is that evergreen trees store food materials in their trunks. It is simpler for these trees to sprout flowers right where the food supply is located than to transmit the food to the upper branches. But the objection to this theory is that the tallest trees would then be most likely to be cauliflorous, and this is not the case.

A different scientific puzzle of the rain forest is the tendency of some trees to develop buttressed trunks. A buttress is a prop or support. In certain rain-forest trees, the roots enlarge and rise above the ground to form big, conspicuous flat plates that are attached to the trunk and seem to be holding the tree steady.

These buttresses take several forms. One type, called stilt roots, springs from the trunk a yard or more from the ground and enters the earth at an angle. There is always an open space between the underside of the stilt root and the ground. Most of the stilt-rooted trees belong to the C level.

Much more spectacular are the bizarre flanged plates, two or three inches thick and several feet high, that spring up around some of the tallest A-level species. Usually there are four or five of these buttresses, more or less evenly spaced around the lower part of the trunk, though there may be as many as ten. The wood of the buttresses is often harder than that of the trunk and may give off a metallic ring when it is struck with an axe. On one Malayan tree, the buttresses reach twenty-five feet or more up the trunk and reach outward for about the same distance. These huge

Stilt roots

Buttress

flat slabs of wood are often cut away and used as large dinner tables.

Perhaps the earliest description of a buttressed tree was written in 1526 by Gonzalo Fernández de Oviedo, a Spanish official in the New World. Oviedo's *Natural History of the West Indies* told of a tree he saw in the Venezuelan jungle "with three roots or parts in the form of a triangle, something like a tripod, and the opening from root to root was more than twenty feet, and it was so high that a side cart . . . could easily pass through any one of the three openings. At a height more than a lance length from the ground the three tremendous trunks or feet came together and formed a single tree or trunk. The lowest limbs of the tree were higher than the tower of San Román of the city of Toledo. From that point on to the top of the tree, there were many large branches. Some Spaniards climbed the tree, and I was among them, and from the point I reached, which was near the places branches began to grow, one could get a marvelous view of the land as it stretched away toward the province of Abrayme. The tree was covered with vines, and these were very safe ladders to climb. Each 'foot' of this tree that I have described was more than twenty spans thick, and where they joined in one trunk the tree was more than forty-five spans in circumference."

Buttresses are grotesque and fantastic sights that fascinate all observers. There is no satisfactory theory to explain their development, however.

The easiest explanation is that they help to support the tree. No doubt they do help the tall trees remain upright. In the rain forest most big trees have widespread, shallow root systems that give them little anchorage in storms, unlike many temperate forest trees that have deep, strong tap roots. In a severe tropical storm these shallow-rooted trees are often thrown over.

But some rain-forest trees have shallow roots and do not grow buttresses. Other species have deep roots and do grow buttresses.

So the buttresses, while useful, do not seem to have developed primarily for support. In any event, the network of vines linking the rain-forest trees is much more valuable as storm protection than buttresses.

If buttresses evolved mainly for support, it is odd that they are found almost exclusively in tropical rain forests, where the density of the foliage reduces the effects even of hurricanes. Why are they not found wherever trees are in danger of being blown over? The giant sequoias of California get along without buttresses. So do the tall, slender eucalyptus trees of Australia, which are the highest trees in the world. Also, within the rain forest the best-developed buttresses are found on trees in shel-

Buttress

tered places, while some trees in windy places have no buttresses
at all. One South American explorer reported that buttressed
trees are in fact blown down more often than those without buttresses.

If these strange woody projections do not really help to support the tree very much, then what are they for?

Scientists have offered many answers. Some are far-fetched
and unlikely; others sound logical but cannot be proved. The
most convincing theory holds that buttressing is the tree's response to strains caused by the wind. As a forest tree sways in
the wind, the roots are stimulated and expand greatly in size to
form buttresses. Close observation shows that this theory has
its merits, but it is still incomplete, for it does not explain why
some species tend to develop buttresses while others do not. Apparently the phenomenon of buttressing is a complex one that
depends partly on wind stimulation, partly on soil conditions,
partly on temperature and humidity, and partly on a given tree's
hereditary tendency to form buttresses.

Another rain-forest novelty is the color of young leaves. The
leaves of many trees are bright red when they first appear, taking
some time to reach the familiar deep green of the forest. Other
species sprout white, violet, or blue leaves. Where many trees
produce new leaves together, the rain forest may take on the
brilliant hues generally associated with an autumn forest in the
north. The red or blue coloring is considered a means of protecting the young leaves from strong sunlight; but this, of course, is
meaningful only for the A-level trees. However, many of the
smaller forest trees also provide fantastic color displays when
their new leaves unfold, and this cannot be explained by the sun-
light-protection theory.

The *sameness* of the rain forest leaves is something that strikes
every observer. With rare exceptions, the trees have long leaves
with smooth edges and shiny surfaces. The leaves vary in size

from tree to tree, but not in shape. It is as if the special conditions of the rain-forest environment have brought every tree's leaves to the same evolutionary stage.

Apparently the smooth tapering outline of the typical rain-forest leaf is the best possible adaptation to a climate of heavy rain and high humidity. Where water collects on the leaves of a rain-forest tree, mosses and fungi quickly take up residence, over-growing the wet leaf until it no longer can manufacture energy for the tree. Therefore the leaf that can rid itself of water most swiftly is the one most likely to endure. The stiff oval leaves of the tropical trees are always more or less moist, but they do not permit the accumulation of pools of water.

Some trees have leaves even more specifically designed for quick runoff of rain water. They have a narrow "drip-tip" at their ends, which serves as a kind of funnel for speedy removal of the water. Drip-tips are most common among the trees of C level. Down there in the darkest zone of the forest, there is little chance that sunlight will dry the wet leaves; the long drip-tips of these trees help them keep relatively free of a surface film of water. B-level trees have shorter drip-tips, and those at the roof of the forest, carrying their leaves into the sunlight, rarely have any.

Within the rain forest we can see nature's response to a special and stable environment. In all but seasonless tropics, a hothouse climate is created that has called forth unique forms of plant life.

The warmth, the high humidity, and the constant rainfall per-mit an astonishing lushness of growth. Trees grow to giant size, and their spreading crowns form a nearly unbroken canopy, robbing the forest floor of sunlight. Below, in the cool, moist darkness of the rain forest, the trees and shrubs adapt to their unusual world. Zones of life take form as each tree reaches its own level of growth. Straight tree trunks stretching toward the sky indicate the struggle for light and life. Flowers and fruits sometimes sprout from woody trunks and limbs; weird gnarled buttresses appear on some trees; leaves take on a common shape.

We do not know why the rain-forest trees have undergone these special responses to their particular environment. But we do know that environment has shaped them. Through millions of years of evolution, the trees of the tropical forests have become perfectly attuned to their dark, wet surroundings.

3

Trees of the Rain Forest

When we walk through a forest of the United States, we do not have to be skilled botanists to recognize most of the trees. Our forests are composed of relatively few species. If we know the oaks, maples, birches, beeches, pines, spruces, and a few other tree families, we can identify the majority of the trees we encounter.

But in the tropics there may be hundreds or even thousands of different kinds of trees in a single forest, many of them similar in form and varying from one another only in flower and seed—impossible to see from the forest floor. Many will have only scientific names, though the most conspicuous will usually have native names as well. Some may have no names at all, for the jungles of the world still hold species unknown to science. How can we possibly know the rain-forest trees?

We can know a few. They stand out because of their unusual appearance or because they have become useful to man. The rest fade into the shiny green blur of the forest and are known only to trained botanists.

Among the trees of unusual form is *Omphalocarpon procerum*, the "cannonball tree" of Africa. A similar tree of the New World jungles, *Couroupita guianensis,* has received the same nickname. The cannonball tree is cauliflorous—its flowers push right out of the heavy bark—and produces long dangling branches on which its fruits are formed. The fruits are hard brown spheres bigger than grapefruits and hang down in clusters. A tall cannonball tree may have dozens of these fruits dangling from its trunk and branches at once. They fall off without warning and can crack a skull, for they are as hard as coconuts. The hollowed-out "cannonballs" can be used for bowls and pots.

Equally strange is *Kigelia pinnata,* the "sausage tree." Found in Africa and the West Indies, this medium-sized tree sends down long cordlike flowering stems on which deep red blossoms appear. The flowers are handsome but have an unpleasant odor; they bloom only for a day, then drop off. Where each flower was, a small gray fruit starts to grow. It keeps on growing for months,

Sausage tree   Candle tree

until it is a huge sausage-shaped object a foot long, weighing ten pounds or more. These odd fruits are not edible, but in Africa their pulp is used externally as a medicine.

Dangling fruit is also a hallmark of *Parmentiera cerifera*, the "candle tree." Unlike most tropical trees, this dweller in the Central American jungles grows branches close to the ground. It is cauliflorous, sprouting flowers on its trunk and branches. The greenish-white flowers produce waxy fruits one to three feet long that have the look and texture of candles, and the pungent fragrance of an apple.

Unfortunately, the candles of the candle tree are not useful. But another cauliflorous tree, *Theobroma cacao*, is very useful indeed. This is the cacao tree, from which chocolate is made.

The cacao tree belongs to the C level of the rain forest. It grows to a height of twenty-five feet and must live in a wet, shady environment. Small pink flowers push through the bark of the trunk and turn into the large, rough red pods that contain the valuable cacao seeds. These, when dried, roasted, and ground, become cocoa and chocolate. (Chocolate contains an oily substance know as cocoa butter, which is removed in making cocoa.)

The Indians of South and Central America discovered the value of the cacao tree more than five hundred years ago. When the Spaniards came to Mexico in the sixteenth century, they found that the Aztecs cultivated the tree in plantations, using taller trees to provide the shade that it normally received within the rain forest. The Aztecs and other Mexican Indians made a drink called *chocolatl* from the ground seeds of this tree.

Chocolatl was very different from any chocolate drink we have today. The Aztecs mixed ground corn into the drink, along with powdered chili pepper and other spices, to get a cold, foaming beverage. The Aztec King Montezuma was enormously fond of the spicy drink, and fifty jars a day of *chocolatl* were prepared in the royal palace. Cacao beans also served as currency in Mexico; a good slave could be bought for a hundred beans..

The Spaniards did not find *chocolatl* to their taste at first, but soon they learned its virtues. "He who has drunk one cup," one of the conquerors wrote, "can travel a whole day without any other food, especially in very hot climates; for chocolate is by its nature cold and refreshing." About 1600, chocolate became a popular drink among the wealthy aristocrats of Spain. But they disliked its peppery flavor, and added sugar instead. Chocolate became the rage in Europe. It was thought to have medicinal values as well as a good taste. A book published in 1730 described chocolate as "very temperate, very nourishing, and of easy digestion; very proper to repair the exhausted spirits and decayed strength; very suitable to preserve the health and prolong the lives of old men." By then, the English had hit on the notion of further sweetening chocolate by adding milk to it. Chocolate factories had opened all over Europe. In 1753, the Swedish scientist and classifier Linnaeus gave the cacao tree its scientific name, *Theobroma cacao*, which means, "cacao, food of the gods."

Wild cacao trees are found in the jungles of Brazil and Central America. Huge cacao plantations have been founded wherever the climate is suitable. Though originally a tree of the New World, cacao has been successfully transplanted to Africa, and more than half the world's supply of chocolate comes from such countries as Ghana and Nigeria. The cacao tree must always be grown in the shade of some taller tree, to duplicate the rain-forest conditions it prefers.

Cacao is often confused with coca, an entirely different South American shrub whose scientific name is *Erythroxylon*. Coca has thick, leathery leaves which have long been chewed by South American Indians to obtain an effect of relaxation and stimulation. White men studying these leaves learned how to extract

cocaine from them. The pain-killing properties of cocaine made
it a valuable anesthetic in the nineteenth century, until it was
found to be a habit-forming drug. Today cocaine is no longer
used in medicine, but the coca leaves still are chewed in South
America for their mild narcotic effect.

Coca automatically brings to mind cola, and this, too, is a
rain-forest product. The cola tree of Africa is a relative of the
New World's cacao tree, and belongs to the same genus, *Theo-*

Cacao

broma. Its nuts contain caffeine, a stimulant, and are chewed by African natives just as coca leaves are in South America. Originally, both coca and cola were used as ingredients for a certain well-known soft drink, but the dangerous drug coca has long since been dropped from the recipe.

Yet one more tree whose seeds are chewed in tropical lands for their stimulating effects is a palm called *Areca catechu,* known in Asia as betel. Throughout the Orient the betel nut is eaten wrapped in betel leaves. The habit is said to be pleasantly relaxing, but few Westerners care to try it, since the betel nut stains the teeth black and the saliva bright red.

Areca catechu, or betel, is one of some fifteen hundred members of the palm family. These trees are almost entirely native to the tropics, though some species are found in the warmer parts of the temperate zones, such as Florida, Arizona, California, and Europe's Mediterranean coast. Palms do not have woody trunks; a palm stem is soft and pithy inside, and covered with a corklike layer outside. A true tree has a growing layer called cambium just beneath its bark, which adds a new ring of growth around the trunk each year. Palms do not have this layer and do not go on growing thicker indefinitely as they get taller. For this reason even the tallest palms are unusually slender and graceful. They never have branches except at the crown, where they bear a tassel of gigantic leaves. Palm leaves are often twelve or fifteen feet in width, and may be as much as fifty feet long.

Most palms are not rain-forest trees. This includes the most famous of all, the coconut palm (*Cocos nucifera*) and the date palm (*Phoenix dactylifera.*) These are both tropical trees, but the date palm thrives in near-desert conditions, and the coconut palm grows outside jungles, often along sandy seashores. The handsome palms used as decorative trees in California and Florida are likewise not jungle species.

In the rain forest, though, some species of palms are frequently found in extensive stands. Many of them are of economic importance. The oil palm (*Elaeis guineensis*) of West Africa yields palm oil, important in soap manufacture. Another African palm provides an oil used in waxes and polishes. The vine palm of Africa and Asia (*Raphia*) is the source of rattan, from which furniture is made. This palm, as its name indicates, grows in the form of a vine, twining over the trunks of trees, sometimes attaining a length of a thousand yards as it reaches toward the top of the forest. It has caused some confusion for explorers who, seeing the familiar crowns of palms high in the forest canopy just ahead, are unable to find the trees to which the crowns belong. Eventually they discover that the leaves belong to climbing palms, lacking even the soft trunk of a palm tree.

Heart of palm, a tender and costly ingredient in salads, comes from a palm of the tropical jungle. The "heart" is the soft growing point of the palm. When it is cut off, the tree dies.

Another jungle delicacy is the young shoots of bamboo. Bamboo is the giant of the grass family; there are many species, found in tropical forests everywhere and also in some cooler parts of the world. Giant bamboo is typically found in the rain forests of higher altitudes and is less common in the lowlands.

It grows in the form of clumps of slender tubelike stems, which bear delicate, narrow-bladed, grasslike leaves. One clump of bamboo may send up dozens of stems, creating an impenetrable thicket all by itself. The growth rate of bamboo in a warm, wet climate is astonishing. The record is held by a jungle bamboo from Ceylon, *Dendrocalamus giganteus,* which was measured as growing sixteen inches in a single day. Some bamboos attain heights of a hundred feet, though usually they are no more than twenty or thirty feet high.

For jungle folk, bamboo is an all-purpose plant. The hollow stems become drinking vessels, cooking pots, pipes, musical instruments, and storage jars. The hard, attractive wood is used for ladders, scaffolds, the beams of houses, fences, spears, arrows, fishing rods, cables, and oars. Flexible young shoots of bamboo can be woven to make furniture, trays, or sails. An English traveler who visited Burma in the nineteenth century reported that the natives lived in bamboo huts, adding, "When I speak of bamboo huts, I mean to say that posts and walls, wall-plates and rafters, floor and thatch, and the withes that bind them, are all of bamboo."

One genus of the bamboo tribe grows native to the United States: the cane-reed, *Arundinaria*, found in swamplands from

Bamboo

Virginia to Texas. These woody-stemmed plants reach heights of thirty feet or more. To see the true jungle bamboo, though, one must visit the rain-forest zone. Giant bamboos form spectacular avenues in Puerto Rico's Caribbean National Forest and may be seen on other islands of the West Indies, as well as in the lands closer to the equator.

Common sights in rain forests, particularly those on the slopes of mountains, are the tree ferns. Ferns are an ancient type of plant life that once formed huge jungles, millions of years before

Tree ferns

any of the modern flowering plants and trees evolved. They stand midway in the scale of plant evolution; they are more advanced than the mosses and fungi, because they have roots and stems that permit them to draw nourishment from the soil, and leaves that manufacture energy from sunlight. But instead of reproducing by flowers and seeds, they produce tiny dustlike reproductive bodies called spores, and that is what sets them apart from the highest group of plants.

Some six thousand species of ferns are known today, found on every continent but Antarctica and in almost every sort of climate. Most of them are small green plants that grow in dark, damp places. In the United States, few ferns are more than five or six feet tall. In tropical forests, ferns grow thirty to fifty feet high, with thick, spongy-looking woody trunks. One tree fern from Norfolk Island, in the Pacific, reaches heights of eighty feet. Tree ferns are most common in Australia, New Zealand, and South America. In the United States, the best place to see them is Hawaii. They also flourish in the rain forests of Puerto Rico, Dominica, and other Caribbean islands.

Strips of stem fiber give the trunks of the tree ferns a shaggy appearance. Frequently the trunk is covered with roots that sprout in midair. Stalks of fallen leaves cling to the upper portion of the trunk, and at the very top is a fan-shaped crown of feathery leaves, ten to fifteen feet in length.

One tree fern found in Java is thickly covered along its leaf stalks and buds by curly, golden-brown "hair." Stories of this fern reached Europe centuries ago and led to an odd botanical myth. It was believed that the "hair" came from a wondrous creature that was part lamb and part plant. Supposedly it looked like a lamb but was connected to the soil by a stalk a yard long. It grazed on the vegetation about it, dying when it had eaten everything within reach. Not until 1725 did a botanist expose this vegetable "lamb" as a hairy fern! The fuzz of this Javan fern, known

as *pulu,* is exported to other countries for use in stuffing pillows
and mattresses. European surgeons use it as a dressing to halt
bleeding.

The rain forest has given man many other valuable trees and
plants. A handsome evergreen about sixty feet high, found in
South and Central America, produces the rubbery sap from which
chewing gum is made. This is the chicle tree, *Sapota achras.* Each
tree is tapped every two or three years, and yields about sixty
quarts of the raw sap. The rough-skinned brown fruit of the chicle
tree, known as a naseberry or sapodilla, is sweet and delicious.

Bengal fig (Java fig)

A large, spreading evergreen tree of Asia gives off another kind of thick sap which once was the world's chief source of rubber. This is *Ficus elastica,* the Indian rubber tree. It belongs to the fig family, which has six hundred members living in tropical and warm temperate regions. Some figs of the rain forest take the form of vines, but others are trees, and one, the banyan, is a truly astonishing tree. This fig of India, *Ficus bengalensis,* begins life in an ordinary way, but sends down woody roots from its branches. When these roots reach the ground, they thicken and become new trunks, so that the original banyan tree is soon surrounded by many additional trunks. A century-old banyan in the botanical gardens of Calcutta has a main trunk twelve feet thick and two hundred additional trunks, covering an area nine hundred feet around. According to an old legend, when Alexander the Great invaded India his entire army of seven thousand men camped under a single banyan tree. Given time, a banyan can become a one-tree forest.

The Indian rubber tree does not have the startling growth habit of its cousin, the banyan. But its smooth gray bark can be tapped for the milky sap that is made into rubber. In India, the trees are tapped when they are twenty-five years old and go on producing sap for the next seventy-five years.

However, today the Indian rubber tree is purely a decorative plant, prized for its large, glossy leaves. Commercial rubber comes from an unrelated South American tree, *Hevea brasiliensis,* the Pará rubber tree. American Indians made rubber balls from this tree's sap before the European conquerors arrived. The Indians called rubber *caoutchouc,* a name that is still occasionally used for it. They tapped the wild trees growing in the Amazon jungle. When Charles Goodyear's vulcanization process made possible the wide use of rubber, early in the nineteenth century, *Hevea* plantations appeared all over Brazil, and there was a wild boom that created many "rubber millionaires." The South Amer-

ican rubber was cheaper and of a better quality than that from
the Asian rubber trees.

For a while Brazil was the world's rubber supplier. The Brazilian government rigidly prohibited any export of the Pará
rubber trees. But in 1876 an Englishman named Henry Wickham
managed to smuggle a few seedlings out of the country and across
the Atlantic to London's botanical gardens at Kew. The trees
thrived in the Kew Gardens hothouse, and eventually new seedlings were shipped from London to British plantations in Ceylon,

Indian rubber tree

Malaya, and Indonesia. Soon the Brazilian rubber boom collapsed. It was so difficult to transport rubber from the jungle plantations of the Amazon to civilization that the new Asian *Hevea* plantations were able to set a lower price for their product. And so the Asian tropics once more became man's source of rubber, though a South American tree had replaced the original Indian rubber tree.

The process worked the other way in the eighteenth century when the breadfruit, an oriental tree, was transplanted to the West Indies. The breadfruit (*Artocarpus incisus*) is a sixty-foot tree which, unlike most tropical trees, bears deeply indented leaves, one to three feet in length, with long finger-shaped projections. Its fruit is round, six to eight inches in diameter, with a yellow warty hide. Its pulp is starchy and tastes a little like potato; it is nourishing and rich in vitamins, and is served fried, roasted, or boiled, usually cut in thick slices.

Breadfruit   Papaya

For centuries the breadfruit—a relative of the fig family—has been cultivated in tropical Asia and on the islands of the Pacific, where the fruit forms a large part of the native diet. In 1789 Great Britain sent an expedition to Tahiti to collect several thousand young breadfruits and bring them to the West Indies. The ship was H.M.S. *Bounty*, the commander was Captain Bligh, and the story is famous. Captain Bligh's crew mutinied, put the commander overboard in an open boat, and sailed for a tropical island. Bligh survived his boat journey and returned to England. In 1792 he made another attempt, this time successful; twelve hundred young breadfruits were gathered and taken eastward to the islands of Jamaica and St. Vincent. Today there are breadfruit trees on nearly every Caribbean island and in Central and South America. They are cultivated as food sources, but occasional wild breadfruits are now to be seen in the jungles of the New World. The botanical garden on St. Vincent displays a huge old breadfruit that is said to be one of the original trees carried to the island by Captain Bligh.

Closely related to the breadfruit is the jackfruit, *Artocarpus heterophyllus*. This tree also comes from Asia, and its fruit is an important food in the tropics of both hemispheres. The weird-looking fruits, a yard long and up to seventy pounds in weight, grow along the trunk of the tree; they are lumpy in shape and are covered with rough ridges. The yellowish pulp is eaten raw, boiled, or fried, and the seeds are roasted like chestnuts. The breadfruit and the jackfruit are valued as delicacies by those accustomed to eating them, but visitors to the tropics who sample these foods rarely ask for a second course. Though breadfruit is nutritious, its texture when fried is approximately that of a thick slice of fried cardboard.

Much more to the taste of northerners is the fruit of the pawpaw or papaya tree, *Carica papaya*. Native to the West Indies and

South America, the papaya has large lobed leaves that resemble those of a breadfruit, and bears clusters of big green fruits at the top of its trunk. The melonlike fruit is a favorite in many parts of the world, as is the juice squeezed from it.

Many other jungle trees are cultivated for their fruit, though few of these exotic fruits ever reach the United States. The Malay apple (*Eugenia malaccensis*) was brought to the West Indies by Captain Bligh with the breadfruit; all over its trunk it grows small pear-shaped fruits which are eaten raw or made into wine. The mammee (*Mammea americana*) is a tropical evergreen that produces large, tasty, brown-skinned fruits which are eaten raw or cooked. More familiar to northerners is the mango (*Mangifera indica*), an Indian tree now distributed through the entire tropical belt. The orange pulp of the fruits is eaten raw or made into canned preserves. Man has cultivated the mango for some four

Mango   Banana

thousand years. The guava (*Psidium guajava*) is another tropical tree whose fruit is shipped to colder countries in the form of jam, paste, or juice.

A double-barreled tree hailing from the rain forests of Indonesia is nutmeg, *Myristica fragrans*. This large evergreen tree, which thrives only in humid conditions, grows small yellow fruits that look somewhat like apricots. Within the fruit is a glossy dark-brown seed contained in a brilliant scarlet wrapper. A spice known as mace is made from this wrapper, and the seed itself is ground to make nutmeg. It takes about thirty nutmegs to produce an ounce of mace.

Probably the most widely consumed of tropical fruits is the banana. Wherever rain forests are found, bananas are grown, but yet the banana is not a rain-forest native. Like corn, the banana is a man-made plant, the product of centuries of careful breeding. Originally developed in India and Malaya, the banana is descended from a wild ancestor that probably had small berrylike fruits. The banana plant grows to the size of a small tree, but what seems to be a trunk is actually a soft hollow stem made of rolled-up leaves. It produces flowers in huge spike-shaped clusters, which become dozens of bananas attached upside-down to a long, dangling stem. Each plant bears one bunch of fruit and then is cut back to the ground.

Like some other plants bred by man, the banana is unable to reproduce itself through seeds. Thus there are no wild bananas. The plant grows from an underground stem called a rhizome; one rhizome can be cut into three or four sections, and a new banana plant sprouts from each. When a banana plant is cut down, a new one soon springs from the old rhizome to replace it. Groves of banana trees are to be seen in many tropical forests, particularly in South and Central America, but they all were established by man after the wild jungle growth was cleared. Bananas were brought to the New World in 1516 from the Canary

Islands, where they had been introduced a few years earlier by Portuguese explorers returning from Africa.

From one of the giants of the forest comes the fluffy floss called kapok, used as stuffing for mattresses, pillows, and life preservers. Kapok is produced by the silk-cotton tree (*Ceiba pentandra*), a native of Africa which may have found its way to the West Indies in the plumage of far-flying birds or, more likely, aboard slave-carrying ships.

In the rain forest the silk-cotton tree is a titan more than two hundred feet high, flanked at its base by enormous tapering buttresses. Its branches begin a hundred feet or more above the ground and stick out awkwardly at right angles. The valuable kapok, as we have already seen, enfolds the seeds in the seedpod of the silk-cotton tree and helps waft them great distances on the breeze. It is a tough, adaptable tree which can survive even in dry country; however, outside the rain forest it may be no more than forty or fifty feet tall.

While scores of tropical trees provide man with useful seeds and fruits, remarkably few are sought for their wood. This is not because of any shortage of good timber trees, but because it is so difficult to harvest them and then to find markets for the wood.

One trouble is that the valuable trees are scattered and lost among the many trees for which man has no special use. In the Philippines, for example, there are over four hundred different forest trees that could be used commercially. But in a forest where there may be more kinds of trees in ten square miles than in the entire United States, it is hard to find a sufficient quantity of any one type of timber to make the operation worthwhile.

Then, too, much of the wood is unsuitable for commercial use. Many rain-forest trees have soft, light wood. Some trees, like the papaya, actually have hollow trunks. Others have trunks containing a pulpy substance, and many large and healthy trees have had their cores hollowed out by insects. Few of these soft-wooded trees are of value. Balsa, the extremely light wood from South America, is an exception.

The difficulty with lumbering hardwood trees is in gaining acceptance for their wood. Pine, spruce, oak, walnut, maple all have ready markets. Exotic tropical woods, usually available only in small quantities, do not. Most of the best-known ones, such as ebony and teak, do not come from rain forests. Until quite recently, one of the few rain-forest trees logged commercially was mahogany (*Swietenia*), which has various species native to Africa and South America. These tall evergreens' hard, handsome wood has long been in high demand.

Lately the tropical woods have come into more favor. Timbermen, long unwilling to conduct logging operations in tropical forests and uninterested in finding out which trees were worthwhile for timber, have greatly expanded their range. Today the wood of some fifty trees is harvested in the tropical jungles. One

Saman

of the finest timber trees is the saman, or "rain tree" (*Samanea saman*). This huge tree, found throughout the tropics both within and without the rain forests, gets its name from the way its tiny leaves close up at night, permitting rain to come through and strike the ground. In the rain forest, a canopy of samans closing at night gives the forest a sudden look of surprising openness. Growing in open country, the saman spreads its branches over a great distance, like a gigantic umbrella. Its wood takes a high polish and makes strikingly handsome furniture.

The rain forests of the world are never likely to become centers of large-scale logging. There are too many problems of operation. A tree with large buttresses must be cut above the buttresses, since it is uneconomical to saw through its greatly expanded base. That means a logging job conducted ten or twenty feet off the ground. Then, too, the trees are so tightly bound together by vines that they may not fall even when sawed through. Or when they do fall, the crash of the mighty canopy brings down dozens of surrounding trees. Loggers must work in clearings, and the dense world of the rain forest resists any attempt at clearing. In Africa and South America, where timber trees are now being logged, it is necessary to keep the forest clear of vines and to remove the lower stories, an endless and taxing job.

4

Climbers, Stranglers, and Others

Some of the most conspicuous plants of the rain forest do not fit conveniently into the arrangement of zones. These are the plants that live on other plants—the vines, the air plants, the fungi, and other hitchhikers of the vegetable world.

Scientists group these dependent plants into three general classes, according to the way the plants obtain their nourishment.

Epiphytes, or air plants, do not have roots in the ground. They make their homes on the branches or trunks of other plants. Epiphytes use their hosts as perches, but do not directly injure them or draw nourishment from them. An epiphyte may grow so large that it weakens or kills its host, but that is only an accidental by-product of the epiphyte's presence.

Parasites live at the expense of others. A parasitic plant is unable to manufacture food for itself, so it connects itself to a plant that can. The host plant carries out the process of photosynthesis, in which carbon dioxide is converted to energy-yielding starch by sunlight and the green pigment called chlorophyll. The host plant is forced to manufacture enough food to provide for its own needs and for those of the attached parasite. If the parasite's demands become too great, the host may die—which means the end of the parasite as well.

Saprophytes, like parasites, lack chlorophyll and so are generally pale, whitish plants. They live on dead organic matter instead of feeding on a living host. Since saprophytes can get along without light entirely, not needing it for photosynthesis, they are dwellers on the forest's dark floor. They take their nourishment from fallen leaves, rotting wood, and other decaying matter. Saprophytes play an important part in ridding the forest of accumulated debris, and in breaking down twigs and leaves into soil they perform a valuable function for the other plants.

Saprophytes and parasites are found in forests all over the world. Epiphytes, though—the air-dwelling plants—are almost entirely tropical plants. The epiphytes include some of the most interesting and characteristic plants of the rain forest.

It is possible for a plant to begin life as an epiphyte and later to send roots into the soil in the conventional way. This, in fact, is what the rain forest's most sinister epiphytes, the strangler figs, do.

There are several species of strangler figs—*Ficus aurea, Ficus brevifolia*, and others—and there are also some stranglers which are not members of the fig family at all, though they behave in the same general way. The life cycle of a strangler begins when a bird or bat high in the forest canopy eats a ripe fig. The small hard seeds pass through the digestive tract and are excreted. Some land on the forest floor and sprout into vines that begin to crawl up the trunk of the nearest tree. When a strangler seed lands on the branch of one of the forest trees, however, it will sprout even in the absence of soil.

A favorite place for strangler seeds to germinate is in a fork between the trunk and a large branch. Soon there is a small bush with glossy leaves. It lives as an epiphyte, mysteriously absorbing nourishment from the humid air. Then the young strangler starts to send roots toward the ground, a hundred feet or more below.

Some of these roots look like thick cables dangling straight down through the air from branch to ground. Others cling to the trunk of the host tree. When they reach the ground, they penetrate it and begin to draw energy from the nutrients in the soil. Now the strangler begins to grow at a frightening rate, like some kind of cancer overcoming the host. The roots clinging to the trunk become thick and woody, branching and expanding, feeding on the bark. Soon the host tree is encased in a wooden sheath

Strangler fig

through which the tree within is visible only in part. High above, the crown of the strangler becomes an opulent canopy. As moisture and minerals flow upward through its vast network of roots, the strangler grows greater in size until it completely chokes the tree around which it has wrapped itself.

The hapless host tree dies and decays. As it rots, the strangler feeds on its wood. Within ten years or so, the original tree has entirely disappeared. In its place stands a mighty fig tree, hollow at the core where the host once was. The descending roots that strangled the host fuse to form a nearly continuous trunk. Some strangler figs reach enormous size, becoming members of the forest's highest story. They bear fruit which the birds and bats of the canopy devour, the seeds are scattered, and the cycle begins again.

Most of the other vines of the rain forest are less murderous. They generally grow from the ground upward, without an epiphyte phase such as many stranglers have, and they rarely if ever kill the host trees on which they twine. They are simply trees with weak stems, which cannot stand alone and must wrap themselves around their sturdy neighbors.

Climbing vines, or *lianas*, give the rain-forest canopy its appearance of phenomenal density. They ascend one tree, disappearing into the mass of foliage overhead, and hang down in monstrous loops, often reaching out to enfold a second tree and then a third, linking them by their crowns. Some lianas are hundreds of feet long, stretching like colossal serpents through the treetops and tying the trees into a permanent alliance. There are lianas as thin and tough as fine wire, and others as thick as a man's arm.

Nearly all lianas begin in the darkness of the forest floor. They are sun-loving plants, and in their early days they are often slender and branchless, conserving their energy as they make their way toward the sunnier levels of the forest. Certain lianas

have entirely different types of leaf in youth and in maturity;
the young leaves are small and velvety, and are held tightly
pressed against the bark of the supporting tree, while after sunlight is reached the vine develops a magnificent crown of large,
glossy, outspread leaves.

Climbing plants ascend their hosts by four main methods.
Twiners have sensitive growing tips which revolve, usually in
the same direction, so that the plants wind themselves securely
around their supports. Young twiners twist themselves around
young trees, for they cannot embrace a tree of great diameter.

Monstera vine

Tree and twiner grow together, and if a twiner is cut away from the host, deep grooves can be seen in the host's bark where the liana squeezed it. Wisteria, found in many northern gardens, is a typical twiner.

Root-climbers have special aerial roots that attach themselves to the surface over which the vine grows. This is how such temperate-zone plants as English ivy and Virginia creeper climb walls. In the rain forest the root-climbers sometimes attach them-

Monstera vine

selves to rocks rather than trees. They generally grow in the forest's lower stories.

Typical of the root-climbers is *Monstera*, a genus of strange evergreen vines of tropical America. *Monstera* encircles the trunk of the host tree with aerial roots, and when it has reached the crown dozens of these roots dangle down like long cords. *Monstera* has large glossy leaves with deep lobes. A novel feature of the leaves are the frequent perforations, an inch or more across. No other flowering plant has perforated leaves. *Monstera* bears edible berries whose taste is said to be halfway between that of a pineapple and a banana. *Philodendron*, a related and similar genus of root-climbers, includes both a small, popular house plant in the north and a giant creeper in tropical forests.

Tendril-climbers have elaborate wirelike tendrils that twine tightly over the supporting surface. Tendril-climbers are best equipped to climb high, and rapidly reach the forest canopy. We can see climbing tendrils on grapevines and pea plants.

Scramblers are vines that lack any special means of attachment, such as tendrils or aerial roots, and that are unable to twine around a host themselves. They climb by looping and entangling themselves in the branches of trees, sometimes putting out branches of their own to hold themselves in place. Scramblers are never very tightly linked to their host. Many of the largest lianas are of this type, and can be seen loosely dangling from the crowns of the tall trees. In the north, the rambling roses are commonly encountered scramblers.

Whatever its method of climbing, the liana has a powerful inner need to get to the upper levels of the forest. Only a few lianas are shade-loving types that coil their way among the C-level trees and shrubs. Ordinarily, when a liana sprouts, it will begin to climb the nearest tree; when no tree is nearby, it will creep along the ground, sending out longer and longer extensions until it finds a suitable host. Some large climbers, if they happen to germinate outside the rain forest where no support is within reach, will grow in the form of short upright shrubs.

Lianas compete with the forest trees for light and moisture. They often slow the growth of their hosts and may cause their crowns to become misshapen or one-sided. The host tree may die and rot away, but by that time the liana has extended itself to the neighboring trees. It is common to see a huge loop of a liana dangling in midair from tree to tree, marking the place where a third tree, once a support for the vine, has disappeared.

Lianas are useful to the jungle dwellers. Their tough, strong stems make good cables, and in many places lianas are used to make suspension bridges across chasms. The stems of climbing palms provide rattan, used for wickerwork baskets and furniture. One family of African climbers has a thick, rubbery sap that once was collected and used as a source of rubber. Another, *Buettneria*, contains cool fresh water, and is sought by thirsty forest rovers. Africans of the Ashanti tribe call it *sukuruwa*, "cup of water." They slice it open and drink from the dripping stem.

A valuable tropical climber is *Vanilla planifolia*, a plant of the orchid family. This vine, a root-climber, grows in either direction: upward from the ground, or downward from a tree's branch. When it starts its life in the air, as is most common, it sends down aerial roots twenty feet or more in length, which dangle in the air and absorb water vapor. These roots are so tough that they can be used for guitar strings. The seedpods of this vine contain the vanilla beans of commerce.

The vanilla plant is unusual among the orchids in that it has the form of a vine. Much more commonly orchids take up residence on the branch of a tree and remain compact in shape. Orchids belong to the type of plants called epiphytes, a name derived from the Greek words *epi* "upon," and *phyton*, "plant."

All the various types of epiphytes have found ways to survive without putting roots in the ground.

The term "epiphyte" is a general one that refers only to a plant's way of life, and does not imply any family relationship between one kind of epiphyte and another. The algae and lichens and mosses that grow as green or gray crusts on rocks and walls are epiphytes. Some ferns in the temperate zone are epiphytes. Only in the rain forests, though, do the most complex members of the plant kingdom—the flowering plants—become epiphytes.

There are several thousand species of flowering epiphytes in the rain forest. Many of these belong to the orchid family or to the family of *bromeliads*, which includes the pineapple. (The pineapple itself is not typical of its family, for it grows on the ground). Unlike lichens, mosses, and other simple plants, the orchids, bromeliads, and similar large epiphytes of the rain for-

Bromeliads

est produce flowers, fruits, and seeds, and otherwise carry on their lives just like any flowering plant of the ground level. The difference is that they live in the air.

Scientists think that the epiphytes of the rain forest may be derived from ancestors which lived under desert conditions. They were accustomed to a great deal of sunlight and could get along with little water or other nourishment from the soil. As these plants moved into the rain forest, they underwent great changes, but retained their liking for sunshine and their relative indifference to the usual sources of nourishment.

Since epiphytes are small plants with a need for light, the only convenient living place for them in the rain forest is on the branches of tall trees. A drifting seed may land in a crack or hollow on the bark of a tree, and an epiphyte sprouts. It does not need much soil or water to thrive. (Many epiphytes do quite well even if they are growing on telephone lines.) An epiphyte needs *some* soil to get started, though. It makes use of the thin layer of dust and decaying debris wedged into the crevices of the bark. These crannies may hold a surprising amount of rotten wood, moldy leaves, dead insects, pieces of flowers, and other rich, nutritious matter. Into this moist layer of humus the epiphyte sends its roots, securely anchoring itself to its host. Other roots reach into the humid air, absorbing moisture from it. The high temperature and high humidity permit these plants literally to drink life from the air.

As they grow, the epiphytes develop other survival adaptations. The spreading roots themselves become collecting stations, catching debris that might otherwise blow away. More humus piles up around the roots. The layer is never very deep, but it is enough to sustain life. Tree-dwelling ants may nest in the roots of the epiphyte, and the bits of leaves they accumulate add to the plant's supply of soil as they decay.

The large, overlapping leaves of the epiphyte form tight bowls in which more forest debris collects and also turns to soil. The encircling leaves may hold water, too. Some bromeliads store a gallon or more of water in their leaves. These watertight tanks, miniature ponds in the forest canopy, may have a variety of residents: worms, snails, the larvae of mosquitoes, even the tadpoles of tree frogs. Thus the bromeliad becomes the home of an entire community of forest creatures.

If a given tree is suitable as a host for one epiphyte, it may

Orchids

just as well be the host for a hundred. And so it happens. A good tree, with the right sort of bark and the proper location, may have its upper branches overrun with epiphytes. Even when dozens of them grow side by side, there is normally no harm to the host. A tree heavily laden with epiphytes is a little more likely to be overthrown by a high wind than one without them; and occasionally a branch may be so weighed down by epiphytes that it breaks off. But these are rare events. It is not to an epiphyte's advantage to injure its host.

The most famous rain-forest epiphytes are the orchids, whose glorious blossoms bring high prices in northern florists' stores. There are some twenty thousand species of orchids, found all over the world from the Arctic to the southern tip of South America. Most, though not all, are epiphytes. In the tropics, orchids can be seen everywhere in the canopy of the rain forest, but the forest visitor rarely gets a glimpse of the showy flowers unless he climbs a tree.

The lovely, grandiose orchids seen in florists' showcases belong to the genera *Cattleya* and *Dendrobium*. *Cattleya* comes from tropical America, particuarly Brazil; the plants have leathery leaves and elaborate flowers ranging in color from purple and rose to lilac and white. *Dendrobium*, an Asian orchid, produces its flowers in long clusters. The giants of the group are the various species of *Angraecum*, from Africa, with flowers twelve inches across and eighteen inches long.

Not all orchids are delights to the senses. There are a hundred orchids of the genus *Bulbophyllum* which are known as "frog orchids." They have small, unattractive flowers and unpleasant odors. An African frog orchid, *Bulbophyllum falcatum*, is said to have "a faint odor resembling dirty feet." Perhaps this is to be preferred to *Bulbophyllum beccarii* of Borneo, whose odor has been likened to that of "a herd of dead elephants."

The bromeliads are a generally epiphytic family of some nine hundred species. They have sharp, quill-like leaves arranged in a circular rosette, and often produce large, conspicuous fruits. The pineapple, a native of Mexico and South America, is one of the few ground-dwelling bromeliads.

Though they are tropical plants, several members of the bromeliad family grow as far north as the subtropical southern states of the United States. Spanish moss (*Tillandsia usneoides*), which festoons trees from Virginia to Texas with long gray streamers, is a bromeliad also found in the rain forests. It rarely produces seeds; new plants are formed when the wind rips the beardlike masses and scatters strands to other trees. The air pines of Georgia and Florida likewise belong to this family. They are small stiff-leaved epiphytes that colonize branches and tree trunks. The bromeliads of the tropical forests are very much like these southern air pines, though much larger.

A plant that is partly an epiphyte and partly a parasite is the tropical mistletoe of the family *Loranthaceae*. This small bushy plant, common in the tropics, is related to the familiar species found in cooler lands. Mistletoe has leaves, stems, and roots, possesses chlorophyll, and is capable of manufacturing its own food like any other epiphyte. But it also has special rootlets called haustoria, which reach into the branches of the host trees and steal sap and water. The damage the mistletoe does is slight, since it borrows only a small part of the nutrients that the host is drawing from the soil. It must live in a high branch so that it can obtain the sunlight it needs for the bulk of its nourishment. In dense tropical forests the mistletoes never grow less than sixty feet from the ground.

They have evergreen leaves and stems that are similar to those of their host trees. Except when they are in flower, they are hard to detect in the rain forest, but at certain seasons they burst forth with masses of brilliant scarlet blossoms. Then they are beautiful to behold. Mistletoes grow as low scramblers in wet conditions, but become much more compact and erect in the drier forests. It is not unusual for one mistletoe to use another as its host, or even for a mostletoe to grow on a mistletoe that is growing on yet another mistletoe.

In northern forests, the evergreen leaves and stems of the mistletoe stand out clearly against the bare limbs of the host in winter. Thousands of years ago in Europe the mistletoe was believed to have magical powers and figured in religious ceremonies. The old legend survives today where mistletoe is used as a Christmas decoration.

A true parasite of the rain forests is *Thonningia sanguinea*, a small African plant. *Thonningia* is able to do entirely without leaves and stem. It consists of an underground rhizome, or rootstock, which sends out sap-sucking haustoria that drill into the roots of forest trees. When it flowers, *Thonningia* sends up through the soil a delicate cluster of blossoms, cream-colored bordered with crimson, protected by sharp projections. There is a related and similar parasite in the South American forests, *Helosis cayennensis*.

Less apparent parasites are certain of the many forest fungi. Fungi—which include mushrooms—are simple plants lacking in chlorophyll. They must, therefore, draw their food from other organisms rather than from sunlight. Some fungi are saprophytic, feeding off dead and decaying matter on the forest floor. Others go directly to living things for their nourishment. They do their work invisibly, sending out rootlike shoots called hyphae, which bore into the roots or stems of other plants. A large tree may endure an invasion of these fungi for many years without harm. But if the tree is weakened by drought or an injury to its bark, the fungi may spread throughout it until they destroy it. The humus collected by otherwise harmless epiphytes often provides the first foothold for these destructive parasites.

The most amazing rain-forest parasite of all was discovered in

1818 by Sir Stamford Raffles, an English diplomat stationed on the island of Sumatra in what is now Indonesia. Raffles, an avid investigator of natural history, led a scientific expedition to Sumatra's rain-forest country, accompanied by his wife and by Dr. Joseph Arnold, an amateur botanist. In the heart of the forest Raffles spied a vast red flower, more than a yard across from petal tip to petal tip. It sprouted without a stem from a host plant. The flower weighed some fifteen pounds, and its central cup could have held a gallon and a half of water.

This enormous parasite, which is adorned by one of the world's largest flowers, now bears the name of *Rafflesia arnoldi* in honor of its two discoverers. Raffles studied its growth and reported that its seeds, carried generally by the feet of elephants trampling through the forest, lodge in surface-lying roots of the shrub *Cissus angustifolia*. When it germinates, it sends roots into the bark of the host shrub and builds its tissues within the other plant. Then it becomes visible as a small round knob which expands greatly in size and is surrounded by layers of tough sheaths to form a huge cup. "The inside of the cup," Raffles wrote, "is of an intense purple, and more or less densely yellow, with soft flexible spines of the same color; towards the mouth it is marked with numerous depressed spots of the purest white. . . . The petals are brick-red with numerous spots of a lighter color. The whole substance of the flower is not less than half an inch thick, and of a firm fleshy consistence."

The dimensions of *Rafflesia*'s flowers are matched only by those of *Amorphophallus*, another genus of the East Indian rain forests. These plants, which are not parasites, have small leaves that spring from an underground rootstock. Nothing about the leaves gives any hint of the monstrous flower that eventually erupts from the ground. The flower is cylindrical when it appears, and in a few weeks it has reached the height of a man. Then it uncoils to become a graceful vase-shaped structure, six to eight feet in diameter and equally high. The vase, yellow without and purple within, becomes the container for a slender yellow column that contains the flower's reproductive organs. This central column reaches a height of fifteen feet.

Aside from *Rafflesia, Thonningia,* and the parasitic fungi, true parasites are rare in the rain forest. Semiparasites, such as the mistletoes, and the nonparasitic epiphytes, are much more common. Also scarce are the saprophytes, those plants that feed on dead matter.

Most of the rain-forest saprophytes are fungi, but there are a few flowering plants. The fungi may be saprophytic or parasitic, depending on local circumstances. They send their threadlike hyphae through dead leaves, twigs, plants, flowers, turning everything to soil as they devour it. Where dead matter is hard to find, they may attack living trees and plants.

The saprophytic flowering plants live on the forest floor or sometimes on dead logs or stumps. Dark, wet places piled thick with dead leaves are their favorites. They often dwell between the angles of a large tree's buttresses. They tend to be small, pale plants of strange appearance. Nearly all are less than six inches high. One exception is a saprophytic orchid that has climbing tendencies and may attain a height of over 120 feet.

The rain forest, then, consists of much more than its three levels of trees. Long looping lianas, murderous strangler figs, brilliant epiphytic orchids glowing in the canopy, tiny saprophytes and parasites—all these belong to the balanced community that is the tropical rain forest.

5

Insects of the Rain Forest

The floor of a rain forest is a dark, secret, sheltered place. It is free from winds, protected from extreme changes in climate, always moist, always relatively cool. Underneath the leafy forest canopy, the forest floor is a busy, thriving, populous place, with ideal living conditions for its billions of inhabitants.

If nothing dwelt on the floor of the forest, it would soon choke in the steady rain of debris from above. Leaves, twigs, fruits, seeds, branches, flowers, buds, animal excrement, and various other things pour down at a rate of several tons per acre per year. But for the creatures that feed on this debris, the trees would quickly be buried in their own cast-off matter.

The creatures of the forest floor are more important than mere garbage removers, though. They are responsible for restoring nutrients to the soil. The trees and plants suck dissolved minerals and vitamins from the soil through their roots. If none of these nutrients ever returned to the soil, but remained locked up in leaves, branches, and trunks, the soil would eventually be lacking in such essential elements of life as carbon, nitrogen, and phosphorus.

76

But the dead leaves and branches and other organic matter that fall to the forest floor contain these vital elements. They are broken down by the insects, bacteria, and other forms of life on the ground, releasing the nutrients. The ground dwellers themselves use only a small fraction of the chemicals they release; the rest is washed into the earth by rain and is drawn up into the roots of trees and plants, beginning the cycle anew. Only through this cycle of growth and decay can the forest endure.

The world at the bottom of the rain forest is a crowded one. Many of its inhabitants are invisible to the naked eye. Bacteria, one-celled animals, algae, fungi, termites, ants, earthworms, centipedes, millipedes, and many others toil endlessly in the tunnels and channels below the surface and under the layer of dead leaves.

Bacteria may number thirty billion per pound of forest litter. They decompose a hundred to a thousand times their own weight in dead matter each day, feeding on the forest debris, while some of the larger creatures feed on them. Little animals called mites and springtails, which can number two hundred million per acre, are among those that eat the bacteria. This, too, is part of the great cycle of the forest. Everything that lives in the forest dies and decays, or is eaten, and becomes food for new life.

The forest insects are the overlords of the forest floor. These six-legged creatures are the largest and most commanding figures of the dark, secret world. Some feed on dead plant matter and help to release the locked-up nutrients; some strip leaves and buds from living plants; some feed on smaller creatures and may even turn on larger animals which intrude on their domain.

The total number of insect species in the world is well over a million, not counting the thousands of unknown jungle species awaiting discovery by science. Insects belong to the phylum, or group, of jointed-legged animals, along with lobsters, spiders, scorpions, shrimps, crabs, fleas, centipedes, barnacles, ticks, mites, and many others. This phylum takes in three fourths of all known animal species. And the rain-forest zone, that warm and humid paradise, contains more different kinds of insects and related jointed-legged animals than any other part of the world.

The most common insect of tropical soils is the termite. These insects, often called "white ants" although they are not ants at all, live wherever there is dead wood to be eaten, but the rain forest is their happiest abode. They are responsible for the rapid breakdown of wood into soil and so are vital to the continuity of the forest.

Termites have an extraordinary way of life. They build huge underground "cities," with miles of narrow, twisting passageways, in which workers constantly move about on errands. Some venture into the upper world to bring back wood, the food of the city. Others clear away dead bodies or dirt in the passageways, keeping everything spotless. The workers are pale in color, almost transparent, and light. They will hide instantly if the termite city is broken open, and the blind, dark, big-jawed soldier termites will come forward to defend the colony against invasion. What they are defending, really, are their king and queen, who live in a clay palace deep in the heart of the city. Workers and soldiers are sterile; all new members of the colony are produced by the gigantic queen, an inch long and thick as a man's thumb, and her royal consort. When the queen is injured, work stops all over the termite city, and if she is killed, the life of the city comes to a halt, the survivors confused and dazed.

No one knows how such news can travel so quickly to the 250,-000 inhabitants of a termite colony, nor what controls the incredibly orderly organization of daily existence in it. Each termite goes about its duties as though receiving instructions from a central planning body. Maurice Maeterlinck, a Belgian playwright and student of insect life, wrote of termites: "Their civilization, which is the earliest of any, is the most curious, most complex, the most intelligent, and in a sense, the most logical and best fitted to the difficulties of existence which has ever appeared before our own on the globe. From several points of view, this civilization, although fierce, sinister, and often repulsive, is superior to that of the bee, the ant, and even of man himself."

Cellulose, the chief component of wood, is the termite's food. Strangely, termites are unable to digest cellulose without help. They must form alliances with other forms of life in order to get benefit from their food. Such an alliance is known as *symbiosis*.

Many of the eighteen hundred species of termites form symbiotic partnerships with microscopic animals called protozoa. Adult termites carry protozoa in their digestive tracts and transmit them to the newborn insects. The protozoa break down the cellulose and allow the termite to draw energy from it; in return, the protozoa get a place to live.

Other types of termites carefully set out beds of chewed wood and let certain saprophytic fungi sprout on them. The fungi break down the cellulose. Then the termites eat the fungi. These underground mushroom beds are maintained at constant temperature and humidity, and the success of the termites in maintaining their cooperative fungi has long fascinated and amazed scientists.

A single termite consumes a little less than two cubic inches of vegetable matter a year. A million termites can dispose of twelve tons of wood a year—the equivalent of an entire large tree, roots and branches. They eat only dead wood, but it does not take long for a fallen tree to vanish before the attack of a termite colony.

Termites build their cities out of clay bound in a cement of their saliva and excretions. The finished product is hard as rock. The walls of a termite city may go thirty or forty feet down into the ground. Some colonies are completely underground; others, particularly in the tropics, jut up ten to twenty feet above the earth.

The termite plays a key role in the everlasting cycle of the forest, returning the nutrients of branches and trunks to the soil so that new tree growth can follow. Unfortunately, termites do not distinguish between the wood of a fallen tree on the forest floor and the wood from which a house is built. So far as the life of the forest is concerned, they are infinitely valuable. But the hungry jaws of termites are a plague to houseowners everywhere.

Termites are often thought to be ants, but though these two groups of insects are similar in appearance and living habits, they are not closely related. Ants, like termites, are social insects that live in large colonies. Each ant in the colony has its special duties to perform. The entire life of the colony revolves around the queen, who is the only fertile female in it.

The rain forests of the world have scores of ant species, most of them much larger than those we are familiar with. The largest ant in the world, *Dinoponera gigantea*, dwells in the Brazilian rain forest. The shiny black females of this species are more than an inch long and are feared for their venomous stings. The male *Dinoponera* is much smaller, brick-red in color, and stays out of sight in the underground nest. These ants are unusual in that their colonies are not divided into soldiers, workers, and queens; each of the big female ants plays all three roles at once.

Most South American jungle plants and animals have their counterparts in Africa. The African representative of the giant ants is *Megaponera foetans*, which is nearly as big as its New World cousin *Dinoponera*. Not only is the African ant armed with a wicked swordlike sting, which can kill an insect or small mammal and cause a man great pain, but it gives off a foul-smelling gas that is poisonous to the termites it feeds on.

These giant ants have long been used in the primitive surgery of jungle folk. Wounds are closed by allowing ants to sink their pincers into the flesh on either side of the cut. Then the ants'

Army ant—*Eciton*

bodies are cut away; the powerful pincers remain attached to the
flesh, holding the wound together as surgical stitches would do.

Dinoponera and its relatives move about on the forest floor as
single individuals, though sometimes a few hundred of them will
form a war party to attack a termite nest or a baby mouse. The
real terrors of the jungle world are the military ants that march
in huge columns numbering millions, destroying every living
thing in their path.

The African members of this frightening tribe are the driver
ants, *Dorylus anomma*. They have no permanent nests, but live on
the march, passing from one region to another and leaving dev-
astation behind. A few scouts go ahead of them, searching for
food. Then comes the army, in a column four or five ants wide
and millions of ants long.

"Advancing at a run," Maurice Maeterlinck wrote of these ants,
"their ranks are enclosed by two living hedges of officers with
large heads and hooked mandibles, who protect and guide and
control them, and at the least alarm, fall upon the enemy. The
movement of these armies, which present, in the world of insects,
a cataclysm comparable to that which would be caused by the
release, in a world of defenseless quadrupeds, of a horde of more
than two million wolves . . . results in a universal and indescrib-
able panic, which is often preceded by flights of birds. All living
things that cannot flee are instantly massacred. A prey too heavy
to be transported is dissected on the spot, and the morsels are
carried off. . . ."

Animals sense the onset of the drivers long before they appear
on the scene. In the jungle, dogs may howl, birds flutter about
wildly. Then come the silent armies, sweeping along the ground,
covering it completely, fanning out to seize food anywhere. The
bite of a driver ant is like the stab of a red-hot needle, and the
jaws do not let go once they have bitten. Nothing but fire stops
the ant invasion. When the army comes to a stream, the ants twine

themselves together to form living bridges, swinging across the overhead branches of the trees.

The forest creatures flee as the drivers approach. Antelopes rush off into the underbrush. Even leopards run away. Elephants snort in fright; their thick hide is no defense against the vicious jaws. The ants climb trees to devour slow-moving poisonous snakes. They sweep through the chicken coop of a jungle village and leave only neatly picked bones behind. They swarm over men who get in their way, nipping at their legs until they fall, crazed with pain, and are devoured. Jungle tribesmen who wish to dispose of an enemy tie him in the path of the drivers and pour a little honey over him. When the ants have passed, just a skeleton remains.

Hungry drivers will eat anything of any size. However, their usual food is insects and small forest creatures: grasshoppers, termites, spiders, snails, cockroaches, other kinds of ants. When they have picked over a few square miles of countryside, they leave it empty of such creatures for weeks or months afterward. Their very hunger makes their own life complicated, for once they devastate a region they must march on for many miles until they come to a new place that can satisfy their appetites.

Two or three times a year, the army halts in its frenzied march and disappears into a hollow log or a hole in the ground, coming together in a compact mass. Surrounded by millions of her subjects, the queen lays her eggs, and new soldiers are born to replace those lost in the endless war against the jungle.

The driver ants are the most dangerous beasts of the African jungle—far more so than the occasional leopards. A leopard kills its prey, feeds, and is satisfied for a while; the drivers move like a fiery tide over a forest, consuming everything in their way.

Not quite so terrifying are the South American relatives of the drivers, the army ants. There are ten species of these ants in the Amazon region alone, varying in color and methods. *Eciton praedator*, a reddish-black ant, organizes its troops in columns a dozen feet wide. The dark brown *Eciton burchelli* moves in a narrower column, while *Eciton rapax* marches in single file. The jaws of South America's *Eciton* ants lack the sharp cutting edges of Africa's *Dorylus*, so that they do not pose the same threat to larger animals. A man or large jungle animal attacked by *Dorylus* will be overwhelmed and slashed in a thousand places before he can move; but it is possible to brush off *Eciton* and escape in time.

To the lizards, snakes, cockroaches, centipedes, frogs, nesting birds, and other small forest creatures, the army ant is a deadly killer. T. C. Schneirla, a naturalist who has studied *Eciton burchelli*, writes that "the approach of the massive *burchelli* attack is heralded by three types of sound effect from very different sources. There is a kind of foundation noise from the rattling and

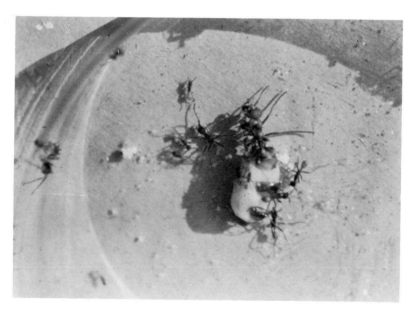

Army ant—*Eciton*

rustling of leaves and vegetation as the ants seethe along and a screen of agitated small life is flushed out. This fuses with related sounds such as an irregular staccato produced in the random movements of jumping insects knocking against leaves and wood. This noise, more or less continuous, beats on the ears of an observer until it acquires a distinctive meaning almost as the collective death rattle of the countless victims. When this composite sound is muffled after a rain, as the swarm moves through soaked and heavily dripping vegetation, there is an uncanny effect of inappropriate silence."

There is another sound—the buzzing of flies that hover over the swarming ants. Now and then the flies swoop down and pounce on the ants. They are not feeding but laying their eggs; with a quick jab the flies thrust their eggs into the live bodies of ants, where they will hatch and develop. Also flying over the army ants are antbirds, which feed on the beetles, moths, and grasshoppers that the ants flush out but do not devour. The antbirds never eat the ants except accidentally, but depend on them to drive other insects into the open.

The army ants, like the drivers, are virtually unstoppable. They surge on up and down ravines, through thickets of wild pineapples, around fallen trees, across streams via bridges of lianas. Most of the members of the swarm are worker ants, a fifth of an inch long. They are the ones that do the real damage, although the soldier ants, half an inch in length and armed with huge pincers that look like tusks, seem much more deadly.

As the ants advance, all living things attempt to escape. For the slower ones—worms, grasshoppers, and such—there usually is no escape. Centipedes, scorpions, and harvestmen ("daddy longlegs") are consumed by the hundreds every moment. Lizards, snakes, frogs, and young birds in their nests also become victims. Where a large animal is tethered in a village barnyard, or is injured and unable to get away, it too is eaten. Some animals and

insects escape by pretending to be dead, for the ants may over-
look a motionless frog or grasshopper. The army ants are blind,
following one another by scent and sound.

During each raid the flow of ants goes in two directions: those
rushing forward to attack, and those streaming the other way,
bearing the booty to the place where that night's camp is to be
made. Legs, heads, wings, bits of flesh and skin, all are carried to
the camp by ants that often stagger under their huge burdens.

By nightfall, most of the ants have arrived at the camp, and
now one of the strangest of all insect nests takes shape. They seek
out a sheltered place—the underside of a log, the opening between buttressed tree roots, perhaps the overhanging edge of a
rock jutting over a stream. The first ants to arrive dig their legs
into any rough or soft surface, anchoring themselves with tiny
hooks. Newcomers hook themselves to these ants, until long hanging ropes of ants are formed, reaching to the ground. The weight
of all these ants pulls the hooks of the first ants deeper into the
anchoring surface. Eventually the ropes adjoin one another until
a solid mass of dangling ants is assembled, a yard or more deep,
wide, and long, containing hundreds of thousands neatly packed
together. Within the cluster the all-important queen is sheltered.
When dawn comes, the ants unhook themselves one by one, and
take their positions in the new raiding columns.

Some species of ants have a strange immunity to the on-
slaughts of these raiders. In Africa, the driver ants cause every
living thing to flee from their path except the red tree ant, *Oecophyllum*. These large ants, which have strong stings and give off
unpleasant odors, make their homes in the trees of the forest
canopy. Their nests consist of leaf fragments pasted together by a
sticky fluid. Only the larvae of the tree ants can produce this
fluid, so in building their nests the baby ants are put to work.
These ants are vegetarians, eating only leaves. Sometimes they
harm a tree by stripping it entirely of foliage, but otherwise they

do no damage in the forest. They use their pincers strictly for defense, and evidently they put up such a good battle that they have no enemies. Forest birds, when hungry enough, may descend to snap up some driver ants despite the risks, but they rarely if ever bother *Oecophyllum*.

W. B. Collins, a naturalist who spent many years in Africa, tells us, "Once, in a spirit of mischief, while idly observing a column of [driver ants] moving across a forest path, I picked a tree ant from a nearby bush and dropped it into the moving column below. I expected to witness its instant annihilation. Instead, to my astonishment, the ranks of the driver ants opened out. Those oncoming promptly stopped, then hastily withdrew, while those on the other side of the red ant continued on their way, perhaps glad to. Soon a diversion was made and the column continued with a bulge: inside the bulge stood the solitary red ant, triumphant.

"Not content, I flung a crowd of driver ants on the single *Oecophyllum*: they fled as though scalded, and indeed they may have been, for there was no doubt that it was not from the red ant's jaws they were fleeing, though it was ready enough to use them. The drivers ran too fast. I then reversed the roles. Selecting the largest soldier among the drivers I placed him on a branch occupied by a dozen or so tree ants. He ran for his life!"

In South America, the ant best able to defend itself against rapacious *Eciton* is *Atta*, the leaf cutter or parasol ant. Leaf cutters, perhaps the most remarkable ants of all, move through the rain forest in long columns just like the drivers and army ants, but they are no menace to insects and lizards. They, like the African *Oecophyllum*, are interested only in vegetation. *Atta's* highways radiate from the nest in all directions. These pathways, bare of foliage, may be seven or eight inches wide and half a mile long. They mark the routes by which the leaf cutters get to their "farms."

Ivan Sanderson, the Scottish-born naturalist who has done much research in South American jungles, writes that "these ants make regular roadways, with underpasses, cloverleaves, and some other engineering . . . works that are still quite beyond us. Admittedly, these appear at first sight just to wander off into the surrounding forest like the paths from the holes of larger animals, but these ants have a very much more direct purpose. The paths lead to trees up which they travel in an endless stream to gather the appropriate leaves at higher altitudes. Then the workers come down again, bearing their loads held aloft like little green sails, and pound solemnly along the highways back to the nest. Traffic is superbly controlled by 'police' ants at intersec-

Leaf-cutter ant—*Atta*

tions and on patrol. If danger intervenes, 'soldier' ants come charging out of the nest and attack the intruder, even if he be a man or other large animal—and the bigger ones can make a neat quarter-inch cut in your flesh. These roads are cleared of every bit of trash, and if something falls upon one, teams of workers are immediately organized to remove it. Thus, they are clear highways at all times. If a large log comes down, the police ants immediately set up detours and get gangs to work clearing a new route under, over, or around the new obstruction."

The purpose of all this feverish activity is to snip pieces out of leaves and carry them back, like big green parasols, to the nest. This work is performed by chestnut-colored females half an inch long, called mediums. They are guarded by much larger females, the maxims, which defend the highways and are accompanied by smaller females only an eighth of an inch long, the minims. When a medium comes back gripping a leaf in her jaws, five or six minims may be enjoying a free ride on it.

No one is quite sure what duties the minims have on the leaf-gathering expeditions, since the mediums do all the work and the maxims do all the necessary fighting. Perhaps they come along simply for relaxation, although ants are not usually in the habit of relaxing. Once the mediums reach the nest, though, tottering under the burdens of leaf pieces several times their own size, the minims go to work.

The nest stands four or five feet above the ground and goes eight or nine feet under the earth. Its outer walls are solid and hard; within, it is a maze of chambers connected by passageways. In these hidden rooms the minims chew the leaves to a fine pulp and spread it out as a compost heap. The pulp is food not for the ants themselves but for a grayish-white fungus called *Rhozites gonglyophora*, which lives permanently in the ant nest. This fungus feeds on the leaf pulp and sends up small round bumps that contain a liquid nourishing to the ants. The ants and the

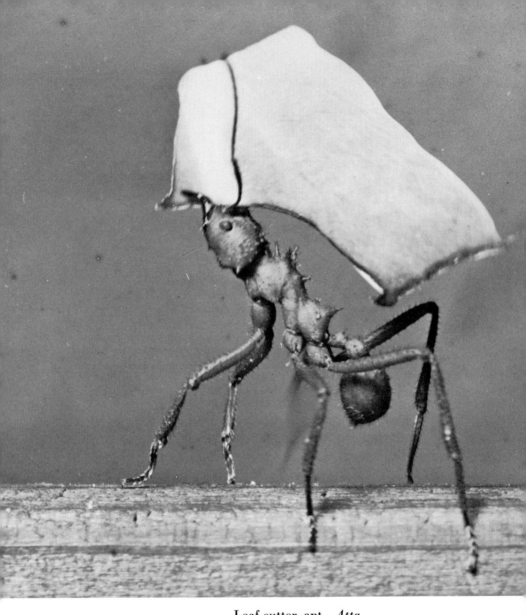

Leaf-cutter ant—*Atta*

fungus thus live in perfect symbiosis; the ants bring leaves to the fungus, chew them up, and arrange them at just the right temperature and degree of moistness; the fungus, in return for this kind treatment, produces the liquid that is the ants' only food.

Back and forth the mediums go, slicing off pieces of leaves to bring to the nest. Any interference, even from a horde of army ants, brings fierce resistance from the maxims. The leaf cutters usually attack trees, sometimes going over a single tree so thoroughly that they leave it with bare branches. (Ordinarily the tree will survive if it is allowed to grow a full new set of leaves before it is attacked again.) However, *Atta* also will attack shrubs, flowers, and cultivated vegetables. In some parts of South America the onslaught is so destructive that the natives are unable to carry on agriculture; leaf cutters simply strip a planted field bare between night and dawn, leaving only naked stalks. Anything else that contains cellulose and is easily cut may be carried away: pieces of clothing, paper, fruit, blossoms. Wood, though, is left for the termites.

The forest has thousands of other insect species. They are found everywhere: in the depths of the earth, on the soil, on tree trunks and shrubs, and in the highest reaches of the canopy. Most are difficult to see, though some, like the crickets, grasshoppers, and cicadas, make their presence known with loud chirping sounds.

Bees of many kinds are found in the forest. The honeybees and bumblebees we are familiar with also live in the tropics, along with the tiny sweat bee of Africa, hardly bigger than a mosquito, and giant bumblebees nearly the size of a mouse. Mosquitoes themselves are no uncommon sights in the rain forest. They love the humid, swampy conditions. One scientist found 150 species of mosquitoes within a five-mile circle in Central America—more than are known to exist in the whole United States. Many of these tropical mosquitoes are carriers of disease, particularly *Anoph-*

eles, which transmits the organism that causes malaria, and *Aedes,* the bearer of yellow fever.

Tropical insects frequently grow to giant size. The world's largest beetle, *Titanus giganteus,* comes from the rain forests of the Amazon. This long-horned monster, five to six inches in length, has savage pincers that can snap a wooden match in half or slash a man's finger to the bone. Each of its six jointed legs has three flat velvety pads equipped with double-pronged hooks; these allow the big beetle to climb trees and make its way through "fields" of jungle moss. Like all beetles, it hides its wings under thick, stiff wing covers. *Titanus* is able to fly, but generally stays close to the ground.

Almost as impressive is *Megasoma actaeon,* a heavy, four-inch-long beetle. The males of this species possess a thick, hard horn that curves forward and upward from the forehead. *Megasoma* is a glossy black in color; much more vivid is another South American giant beetle, *Acrocinus longimanus,* the harlequin beetle. It is three inches long, with slender antennas nearly three times the length of its body, and huge legs. The wing covers are olive green, with a pattern of red markings outlined in black. Splashes of red brighten the joints of the exaggeratedly long legs. The large blue eyes are bordered with a red, black, and yellow trim, giving the harlequin beetle's face a masklike appearance.

Beetles of every imaginable shape and color are to be found in the tropics. There are more than 270,000 known beetle species in the world—the largest single order in the animal kingdom—and the majority of these are tropical.

Many creatures share the forest floor with the ants, termites, beetles, and assorted other insects. Earthworms, blind and simple animals, glide through the soil, swallowing earth and straining food from it. The earthworms of West Africa reach lengths of a yard; the giant Australian earthworm, *Megascolecides australis,* sometimes is twelve feet long. They feed on bacteria, fungi, pro-

Giant Beetle—*Titanus giganteus*

tozoa, and other small inhabitants of the soil, and help to enrich
it by turning them into fertile humus.

Millipedes look like earthworms with dozens of legs, but they
belong to a higher order than the worms. Their name, which
means "thousand-footed," is nearly an accurate description of
them; some millipedes have 350 pairs of legs. They are slow-
moving creatures a few inches long that live hidden under stones
or fallen leaves. Harmless vegetarians, they munch dead leaves
and bits of bark, and try to keep out of sight as much as possible.
Their relatives, the centipedes, have fewer legs—thirty-five pairs,
on the average—and are much more aggressive. Centipedes (the
name means "hundred-footed") are fast-moving and fierce, feeding on insects and worms. Many are equipped with poison fangs.

Scorpions belong to the same group of animals as centipedes
and millipedes. The imperial scorpion of the humid tropics,
Pandinus imperator, is an ugly, clumsy creature with four pairs
of walking legs and a pair of pincerlike claws that can be as large
as those of a lobster. A long, muscular, jointed tail bears a poisonous sting in its tip. A hunting scorpion carries its tail arched
forward over its back; it strikes swiftly, and the venom is fatal
to a small animal such as a mouse or a snake, painful and para-
lyzing even to a man. When the scorpion has killed or stunned its
prey with its sting, it feeds by sucking its victim's body fluids.

Spiders also are forest killers. There are many types, some so
small as to be nearly invisible, others six inches across and
covered with thick furry hair. All have eight legs, and all hunt
for their food. One genus, the African *Theraphosa*, will attack
and eat even large birds.

Through the depths of the forest slink a host of other small
creatures—snails, flatworms, crabs, and many more too numerous to discuss. Most of them take care to keep well hidden. In
the humid air fifteen or twenty feet above the ground are the
winged insects—clouds of gnats, flies, mosquitoes. Still higher, in

the lofty canopy, are populations of tree-dwelling insects of species entirely different from their relatives on the ground.

And on all levels of the rain forest are the most graceful and elegant of the forest insects, the butterflies. Nowhere else are there so many butterflies or such beautiful ones. Henry Walter Bates, the nineteenth-century naturalist who spent more than ten years collecting insects in South America, found seven hundred species of butterflies within an hour's stroll from the Brazilian town of Pará. All of Europe, with its 3,800,000 square miles, has fewer than four hundred species.

The undisputed showpieces of the butterfly world are the *Morphos*, with gorgeously colored wings often seven inches across. "It is a grand sight," Bates wrote, "to see these colossal butterflies by twos and threes floating at a great height in the still air of a tropical morning." They rarely flapped their gleaming wings, simply drifting for long distances. *Morpho rhetenor*, said Bates, had wings so glittering it dazzled the eye to look at them. Sunlight reflected off the wings of *rhetenor* could be seen a quarter a mile away. It was hard to capture, for it rarely came lower than twenty feet. Another, *Morpho eugenia*, with satiny-white wings, was equally difficult for Bates to catch. But when he moved further inland in the forest, he found the butterflies less wary. "In certain places on the road," he said, "I found them by dozens sitting on the ground or on twigs by the roadside and could easily have captured a dozen or twenty a day if I had wanted them."

Everard im Thurm, a British traveler who lived in Guyana in the 1880's, called the *Morphos* the most striking of all butterflies. He wrote of "the huge *Morphos*, the large wings of which are entirely blue, and so gorgeous, brilliant, and shining, that the insect as it comes flaunting lazily down through the dark alleys between the tree trunks seems even from a considerable distance like a flash of blue light. They generally fly high, at the tops of the trees; but for a short time every morning, apparently when the sun is at a particular point in the horizon, they come down into the open."

Only the male *Morpho* boasts these colorful, metallic wings. The females are quite dowdy and inconspicuous.

Among the many gaudy tropical butterflies, the ones most likely to be noticed after the *Morphos* are the *Heliconias*. These South American butterflies have long narrow wings unlike those of most others of their kind. Bates, who saw them in Brazil, wrote, "The prevailing ground color of the wings of these insects is a deep black, and on this are depicted spots and streaks of crimson, white, and bright yellow, in different patterns according to the species. Their elegant shape, showy colors, and slow, sailing mode of flight make them very attractive objects, and their num-

Glass-winged butterfly

bers are so great that they form quite a feature in the physiognomy of the forest, compensating for the scarcity of flowers."

Not all the rain-forest butterflies boast these rainbow hues. Down in the ghostly gloom of the forest floor, butterflies flit about that are a dull, mousy gray or brown in color. Weirdest of all are the glass-winged butterflies, which flutter just above the ground in the deepest, darkest, thickest part of the jungle. The wings of most butterflies bear flat scales that contain the colors. The wings of the glass-winged butterflies have these scales greatly reduced in size and number, and in some cases set on edge like the open slats of a Venetian blind, so that the transparent wing is not hidden. Patterns of color can be seen along the edges and veins of the wings, but elsewhere they are so clear that one can easily read through them.

The people of the jungle solemnly believe that the glass-winged butterflies are the spirits of dead children. This belief is widespread in tropical America, and a scientist who tries to collect these insects when natives are around may find himself in considerable danger.

It is not hard to see the origin of the legend. The glass-winged butterflies are dimly visible, no more than spots of light, as they move above the ground. Now they are here, and now they are gone, fading into the background. They look indeed like ghosts, the souls of lost children drifting eerily through the dark silence of the forest.

6

The Jungle Creatures

The first time one visits a tropical forest, the absence of large animals is always puzzling. Where are the jungle creatures? Where are the lions, giraffes, tigers, gorillas, chimpanzees, elephants, and the rest of the jungle menagerie? Where are the parrots and other flashy birds? On my first venture into a rain forest, the largest animal I saw was a tree snail, about the size of a fifty-cent piece. Where were all the others?

Some were there, well hidden. Others never were jungle animals in the first place. Most of the animals of the tropics live on the fringes of the jungles, along riverbanks and lakes, or else outside the forest completely. The closed canopy of the forest contains a good deal of animal life, but not nearly so much as is found outside.

Lions and giraffes are animals of the plains, not of the jungle. Gorillas and chimpanzees are found only in African forests; the New World has none of the great apes, only monkeys. No elephants have lived in the jungles of the Western Hemisphere for thousands of years. Despite this, there is an abundance of animal life in any rain forest. One needs only to know where to look.

It is nearly as strictly zoned as the plant life. There are canopy dwellers, ground dwellers, and those that live in the B- and C-level trees in between. Rarely does a canopy dweller come down to the ground, and even more rarely does a ground dweller climb to the forest roof. (It would be very unusual to see an elephant sitting in the crown of a tree.) Only the animals in the middle zone go upward or downward when seeking food or a safe hiding place.

The canopy, that arching green vault across the forest's sky, is home to a great many creatures. But the canopy is almost inaccessible to scientists, and until recent years little was known of living conditions there. As late as the 1920's the naturalist William Beebe wrote, "Yet another continent of life remains to be discovered, not upon the earth, but 100 to 200 feet above it, extending over thousands of square miles. . . . At present we know almost nothing about it. Up to now gravitation and tree trunks swarming with terrible ants have kept us at bay, and of the tree-top life we have obtained only unconnected facts and specimens. There awaits a rich harvest for the naturalist who overcomes the obstacles—gravitation, ants, thorns, decayed trunks—and mounts to the summit of the jungle trees."

Since those words were written, many scientific teams have risked life and limb to enter the forest canopy. Using line-shooting machines and rocket-firing guns, they have thrown ropes over the branches a hundred feet up, and with pulleys and iron spikes have hauled themselves upward to invade the canopy world, often spending weeks in tree houses there. As a result, that world is no longer unknown to us, though it holds many mysteries.

The view from the top of a forest giant is entirely different from the view on the ground. R. W. G. Hingston, the leader of Oxford University's expedition to the rain forest of Guyana, wrote in 1932: "The canopy viewed from the above presented itself in the form of a vast plain with plenty of color, not indeed a

level plain, but rather a somewhat undulating surface with eleva-
tions and depressions in accordance with the varying levels of
the ground and the different heights of the trees. Every shade of
green was represented, and many of the young leaves were cop-
per, yellow, or brown. Flowers, too, were evident in abundance,
and of varying shades of purple, pink, and white. The roof top
presented an altogether different picture from that of the flower-
less forest underneath. There were vultures and swifts circling
above it, parrots and humming birds alighting in its foliage, insects and spiders on the branches close at hand."

This is the world of the agile: monkeys, squirrels, birds, bats.
It is a strange world where squirrels fly nearly as well as birds.
The birds, most of them, are on their way toward forgetting how
to fly. They hop around from branch to branch, digging in with
their claws and getting an extra grip with their beaks. When a
snake or some other hungry enemy appears, they scuttle rapidly
through the foliage, running and dodging and hardly ever taking
to flight.

What attracts birds to the forest canopy are the flowers and
fruits. Some live on nectar, others eat fruits, still others dine on
the insects that visit the flowers. While these birds make their
way through the dense leaves of the treetops, hawks and eagles
drift in the sky far above, suddenly diving down to seize one of
them. With such foes cruising overhead, the birds of the canopy
try to remain hidden inside the canopy and avoid exposing themselves on top of it.

Strangest of the forest birds is the toucan, the bird that is
mostly beak. There are seventy species of toucans. Each has a
gigantic, gaudy-colored bill that would not be out of place on a
bird five times its size.

"You will be at a loss to conjecture for what ends nature has
overloaded the head of this bird with such an enormous bill,"
wrote Charles Waterton, who saw toucans in South America in

1812. "The flight of the toucan is by jerks; in the action of flying it seems incommoded by this huge disproportioned feature, and the head seems as if bowed down to the earth by it against its will; if the extraordinary form and size of the bill expose the toucan to ridicule, its colors make amends." Stripes of yellow, red, black, and blue decorate the comically huge bill, which is actually spongy in structure, quite light, and much less of a burden for the bird than Waterton thought.

Why does the toucan have such a mighty beak? No one has clearly determined this. Waterton thought it served no use at all. It is too weak for defense, too clumsy for cracking nuts, tearing flesh, or scooping up food. Ornithologists today are inclined to think that the toucan's long beak allows it to reach food on small branches too light to support the bird's weight, but that still does not seem sufficient explanation for such a phenomenal appendage.

Toucan

Another winged curiosity of the South American rain forest is the hoatzin, which looks like something out of a prehistoric era. Modern birds are descended from reptiles, and none shows this more clearly than the hoatzin, which looks like a lizard with feathers and wings. Instead of flying, which it can barely do, it moves through the treetops using its feet and wings. Young hoatzins are featherless and have three sharp curved claws on the front edge of each wing, allowing them to make their way rapidly from branch to branch to nibble tender leaves.

The hoatzin is about the size of a large pigeon, with an olive-green back and a dull red belly. From its head sprouts a high comblike crest of yellow feathers. It stays close to water, living in the trees and shrubs along the banks of jungle streams, and

Hoatzin

spends much of its time swimming. When it must fly from tree to
tree, it leaps into space with a weird froglike croak, fluttering its
wings desperately until it reaches a new perch. A long flight—
say, fifty feet—so exhausts it that it may make a forced landing
on the ground to rest, midway in the journey. Clumsy though it
is, the hoatzin has few enemies, because it has an unpleasant
smell and taste. South American natives call it the stinkbird.

Other forest birds are less grotesque but just as colorful. There
are the parrots and macaws, with their bright feathers of red and
green. There are caciques, big birds related to orioles, whose
nests are long dangling pouches swinging from the high branches.
There are hornbills and curassows and frogmouths and goat-
suckers and hummingbirds and hundreds of others, making a
marvelous procession of rainbows from dawn to dusk. Some, like
the tiny hummingbirds, seem to remain aloft all the time, but
most shun the air and clamber through the branches of the
canopy. Even birds that are good flyers, like the parrots, pass
most of their lives in the treetops. A parrot's powerful beak is designed both as a superb nutcracker and as a means of holding on
in precarious places.

Some winged creatures of the canopy are not birds. Many species of bats live there. And bats, though they can fly, are mammals, warm-blooded animals that nurse their young. They are
everywhere in the jungle: under the leaves of trees, inside hollow
trunks, in caves, beneath rocks. They sleep by day, come forth at
night to gather food.

Ivan Sanderson describes how the great bats, *Megachiroptera*,
invade the forest canopy: "When certain choice fruits ripen on
the canopy great hordes of them, tens of thousands strong, may
come over at dusk and descend upon the feast. Their fluttering,
scrambling and chomping can become almost deafening, and a
continuous shower of rinds, pits and juice comes pouring down
on you from on high. . . . A horde of them cleaning out a tree can

be heard a mile away even though sound does not carry well in the jungle."

It is rare that anyone gets a good look at a bat in broad daylight—and just as well, for most of them have faces that could have been conceived in nightmares. Huge ears, tiny eyes, gaping toothy mouths—a gallery of bat portraits shows nature's imagination in a mood of fantasy.

Terrifying as they look, most bats are small and harmless eaters of fruit and insects. The one that has had the worst publicity is the vampire bat, whose bloodsucking traits have been greatly exaggerated.

Early explorers did not even know which bats were the vampires, and generally ascribed the habit of drinking blood to the largest and most diabolical-looking species. Thus in the late nineteenth century the African explorer Richard Burton, a man who should have known better, declared that it must be ghastly "to awake suddenly and to find on the tip of one's nose, in the act of drawing one's life blood, that demoniacal face with deformed nose, satyrlike ears, and staring fixed saucer eyes, backed by a body measuring two feet from wing-end to wing-end."

Vampire bat

Burton had never been to South America, where the vampire bats come from, and he fell into the old trap of thinking that the biggest and ugliest bats must be the bloodsuckers. Actually, the large bats, with wingspreads of two to three feet, are innocent of the charge. They feed only on fruit. There are three genera of vampire bats—*Desmodus, Diphylla,* and *Diaemus*—and all are small creatures, about four inches in body length, with wingspreads of a foot or so.

Vampires are parasites. Their digestive systems are unable to handle solid food, and they swoop down at night on sheep, cattle, chickens, pigs, horses, dogs, or any other available animal—including human beings—to draw blood. Their front teeth are sharp as razor blades and are curved in such a way that with a few quick nibbling bites they can scrape away the skin and expose the tiny blood vessels beneath. Contrary to general belief, vampires do not suck blood from their victims. They make round, shallow punctures from which the blood flows freely, and lick up the blood with their tongues as it spreads over the victim's skin. The whole process is done so rapidly and delicately that a sleeping victim rarely awakes. Alfred Russel Wallace, who was bled twice by vampire bats while living in tropical jungles, declared, "In neither case did I feel anything, but awoke after the operation was completed."

Like wise parasites, vampires never take so much blood at any one time that their hosts are seriously weakened. However, several bats may visit the same host in a single night, or may return night after night until the victims suffer from loss of blood. Farm animals in tropical regions of South America are often severely impaired by too-frequent bloodletting. The chief harm done by vampire bats, though, is not the stealing of blood but the transmission of disease. Like ticks, mosquitoes, and other blood-drinking parasites, bats carry harmful microorganisms that enter their victims' bloodstreams. A form of rabies transmitted by vampire bats is a grave medical problem in South America.

Other mammals of the canopy level lack wings, but have their own methods of "flying." Flying squirrels of several varieties possess furred flaps of skin between their limbs; when they must make a sudden jump, they spread these flaps and glide for astonishing distances. Such animals as the flying mouse of Africa (*Idiurus*) and the kobego of Asia can fall a hundred feet or more from canopy to forest floor without suffering injury, floating gently all the way down.

Since these winglike flaps have no muscles, they cannot be operated as true wings, and their owners are unable to fly in the real sense of the word. They are superb gliders, though, and find it simpler to get from one tree to the next by jumping and floating than by climbing. They glide upward with difficulty, and really determined enemies can force them to the ground by making them leap from tree to tree, losing altitude each time. Once on the ground, they are almost helpless, since the large floating membranes interfere with their motions.

The monkeys of the canopy do not have the ability to glide, but in place of flaps they have something nearly as useful: a tail so agile that it serves as a fifth limb. Tails of this sort are called prehensile, from the Latin word *prehendere,* "to lay hold of."

A prehensile tail is a handy thing to have. When an animal is swinging from tree to tree a great distance above the ground, it is certainly true that five hands are better than four. The tail, always poised and ready, will wrap itself around a branch in case its owner loses balance or misses a jump. It can be used for conveying food to the mouth, for brushing away insects, or for combing the fur. Mothers grip their babies with their prehensile tails; sleeping animals moor themselves tightly to branches with them. A monkey whose arms and legs are busy collecting food can hang by its tail while occupied.

Considering all these uses, it is surprising that prehensile tails are found only in the New World. One animal from Australia, which is not a monkey, is the lone exception. Whenever you see a monkey dangling by its tail, you may be certain that it is a native of tropical America. Even in South America, only one monkey species out of three has a prehensile tail. (Several other kinds of canopy dwellers in South America have such tails, including the kinkajou, a relative of the raccoon, and the opossum. There is even a tree-dwelling tropical porcupine with a prehensile tail.)

Most New World monkeys are quite small. The biggest is the howler monkey, *Mycetes*, a reddish animal about two feet long that weighs some thirty pounds. As monkeys go in Asia and Africa, this is not large at all. The howler, a solemn-looking ani-

Howler monkey

mal with remarkably human features, makes up for its small size
with its huge voice. All night long the improbable bellowing of
the howlers resounds through the jungle. They take their posts
in the topmost branches and let loose an appalling symphony of
deafening roars.

At first it is impossible to believe that one medium-to-small
monkey can make so much noise. Ivan Sanderson described the
nightly song of a howler monkey as "like half a dozen jaguars
having it out in a large, tiled bathroom." Charles Waterton wrote:
"You would suppose that half the wild beasts of the forest were
collecting for work of carnage. Now, it is the tremendous roar of
the jaguar, as he springs on his prey; now it changes to his terrible and deep-toned growlings as he is pressed on all sides by
superior force; and now, you hear his last dying moan, beneath
a mortal wound." To the naturalist William Beebe, the howlers
as they tuned up produced "a low soft moaning" that "comes
through the forest like the forewarning of a storm through pine
trees. This gains in volume and depth until it becomes a roar.
It is no wind now, nor like anything one ever hears in the north;
it is a deep, grating, rumbling roar—a voice of the tropics; a
hint of the long-past ages when speech was yet unformed."

The secret of the howler monkey's incredible voice is a unique
sound box in its throat. A thin-walled bony cup that protrudes
like an oversized Adam's apple serves as a built-in loudspeaker,
amplifying the monkey's sounds.

From the South American rain forests comes the world's
smallest monkey, the pygmy marmoset. Full grown, it stands less
than three inches tall and weighs about four ounces. Marmosets
are gentle, delicate animals that make high chirping sounds.

Among the other inhabitants of the South American forest
canopy is the small capuchin or white-faced monkey, the one em-
ployed by organ-grinders all over the world. Its tail is only partly
prehensile, but it has well-developed hands, and is the most rest-

lessly active of all the jungle creatures. Perhaps it was the inspiration for William Beebe's definition of a monkey: "An animal which never wants to be where it is."

Capuchin monkeys move in flocks of four or five hundred through the highest reaches of the forest, making prodigious leaps from tree to tree. Henry W. Bates, watching capuchin acrobatics along the Amazon, wrote: "When the foremost of the flock reaches the outermost branch of an unusually lofty tree, he springs forth into the air without a moment's hesitation and alights on the dome of yielding foliage belonging to the neighboring tree, maybe fifty feet beneath; all the rest following the example. They grasp, on falling, with hands and tails, right themselves in a moment, and then away they go along branch and bough to the next tree."

The spider monkey of South America has the most prehensile of tails—a long, wiry one whose underside is bare and highly sensitive. This small monkey, with a pinched, drawn, suffering expression on its face, seems to be all arms, legs, and tail, having hardly any body at all. Unlike most monkeys, which have the advantage of an opposable thumb that permits the hand to close as a human being's does, spider monkeys have undeveloped and often entirely absent thumbs. Thanks to their remarkable tails, this is no handicap. Few monkeys can move as swiftly or as boldly through the trees.

The lack of a prehensile tail, on the other hand, causes few problems for the monkeys of Asia and Africa. To compensate, they have well-developed hands with strong thumbs. Though they cannot wind their tails around branches, they use them as stabilizers and supports. The black colobus monkey of Africa has a tail five feet long, which it employs almost as if it were prehensile.

The big apes—gorillas, chimpanzees, gibbons, orangutans, and such—get along without tails entirely. The gibbons, which are smallish, slender apes with extremely long arms, are canopy dwellers in the rain forests of Asia and Indonesia. Bulkier apes like gorillas and chimpanzees spend most of their time on the jungle floor, although a chimp can scramble to the top of the forest when the whim strikes, and gorillas will climb trees to sleep in them.

The monkeys, birds, and bats have many neighbors in the crowded canopy. Snails, frogs, mice, rats, snakes, lizards, and others are all permanent residents, and there are frequent intruders from below, since nearly every forest creature is a capable climber. Ivan Sanderson, who spent two weeks living 120 feet up in a tree house in the Nicaragua jungle, wrote that "the most noticeable feature of the canopy, or rather, the one that finally impressed us most, was its traffic. I had always supposed that the canopy, being a continuous flying continent, since it is bound inextricably by interlocking branches and massive lianas, would present a more or less endless field for movement, at least for small animals. Not so! Just like the domain of the ground-living animals, it proved to have regular highroads with subsidiary feeder paths to food areas. What is more, all the animals seem to know, and stick to, these highways—from jaguars and monkeys and leopards and apes, to arboreal [tree-dwelling] rats and mice, snails, frogs, and insects. This was brought most forcibly to our attention when we discovered that we had built our modest platform and taken up residence at a five-way intersection."

Sanderson tells of invasions of his temporary home by hordes of animals who were accustomed to passing through that intersection: first the tree frogs, then the snails, then the monkeys. Capuchin monkeys danced across the platform and flung food and scientific specimens playfully to the forest floor.

Just beneath the crowded world of the topmost canopy are the B-level trees. Here, in the middle tiers of the forest, about fifty

Pangolin

feet above the ground, lives a different group of creatures. This zone is the most densely populated of all, for beside its special inhabitants, it is often visited by animals whose normal home is above or below.

Some of the forest's most distinctive creatures reside in the middle tiers. Moving slowly along the branches is something that looks like a walking pine cone the size of a cat; it is the pangolin (*Manis*), a mammal of an extremely ancient type. Four species of pangolins live in Africa, and one each in India, China, and Malaya.

Thick, horny scales cover the pangolin from the neck to the tip of its long, heavy tail. A French traveler named Desmarchais, who saw a pangolin in the forests of Guinea in the eighteenth century, reported that the scales "are shaped very much like the leaves of artichokes only somewhat more pointed. They lie close together and are thick and strong enough to protect the animal from the claws and teeth of other animals." When attacked, a pangolin rolls up tight and wraps its scaly tail over its belly. Not even a leopard is able to get past the sharp scales.

The pangolin has no teeth, and eats nothing but insects, crawling through the trees and lapping them up with its sticky tongue. Strong claws enable it to grip the branches. Only when it is really hungry will it leave the safety of the trees and venture to the ground, where it shuffles along in an awkward hopping motion, counting on its armor to protect it while it searches for the nests of termites or ants.

Almost as toothless and equally sluggish is the tree sloth of the Americas. Two types of sloth exist today, the two-toed sloth of South America and the three-toed sloth of Central America, the last survivors of what was a large and widespread animal family millions of years ago.

Sloths are found clinging upside-down to the limbs of forest trees. They are about the size of large dogs, with arms that are much longer than their legs. Their heads are round, their noses are stubby, and their small eyes have a look of wondrous stupidity. For a tail they have a buttonlike stub about an inch long.

On the ground, a sloth is almost unable to get about. It drags along clumsily, walking on its knuckles with its long, sharp claws tucked underneath. In a tree, though, it moves ably if not precisely with vigor. It crawls from one branch to the next in a motion that has been described as "like a sailor going up a rope, hand over hand," digging its claws firmly into the next bough before letting go of the last. The customary position for a sloth, when it is not climbing, is suspended from the underside of a branch. A sloth eats, sleeps, relaxes, and usually moves about all in the same upside-down position. Baby sloths, when reared by their mothers, hook their claws into her fur and similarly hang upside down. "If there is anything odder than an upside-down sloth," one naturalist has written, "it must be an upside-down baby sloth hanging to the back of its upside-down parent."

Tree sloth

Sloths have no front teeth, and those in back are poorly developed, lacking roots and enamel. They feed on leaves and tender twigs. Gonzalo de Oviedo, the sixteenth-century Spanish chronicler of the natural history of the New World, wrote that if a sloth settles comfortably in a tree, "it will remain there eight or ten or twenty days. No one can find out what this animal eats. I had one in my home, and from my observations I have come to believe that this animal lives on air. There are many people in the New World who share this opinion, for the sloth has never been seen to eat anything, but it turns its head and mouth into the wind more often than in any other direction, from which one can see that it is very fond of air. It does not bite because its mouth is too small; nor is it poisonous. I have never seen such an ugly animal or one that is more useless."

Sloths do not really live on air, of course, but they go for long stretches of time without eating anything, or, indeed, without doing anything. Their motionless life evidently does not cause them to work up much of an appetite. Small plants called pleurococci grow in their fur, giving them a greenish tint that camouflages them in the trees. There they hang, hooked on tight, taking little part in the life of the tropical wilderness.

The African potto (*Perodicticus potto*), another animal of the forest's middle tier, might almost be considered a relative of the tree sloths. It is about the size of a cat, looks very much like a teddy bear, and crawls upside-down along the branches, munching on leaves. Willem Bosman, a Dutch merchant who explored Africa about 250 years ago, said the potto was "known to us by the name of Sluggart . . . a whole day being enough for it to advance ten steps forward. Some writers affirm that when this creature has climbed upon a tree he doth not leave it until he hath eaten up not only the fruit but the leaves entirely; and then descends fat and in very good case in order to get to another tree; but before his slow pace can compass this he becomes as poor and lean as 'tis possible to imagine, and if the tree be high or the way distant and he meets nothing on his journey, he invariably dies of hunger between one tree and the other. This is such a horrible ugly creature that I don't believe anything besides so very disagreeable is to be found on the whole earth."

Bosman to the contrary, the potto is not truly so slow-moving that it can starve to death between one tree and the next, nor is it really so ugly; pottos are actually rather appealing little animals with big shining eyes and small pink noses. But they are slow enough and never leave the trees if they can help it, somehow managing to get from tree to tree as they feed. Their fingers are long and extremely strong, and are opposable, allowing them to hold to a branch with amazing force. African natives call the potto "the one who will not let go."

Those opposable fingers give a clue to the potto's place in the animal family. It is no relative of the sloth but belongs to the primates, the most advanced group of animals, which includes not only the nimble monkeys and the massive gorillas but also man himself.

The galago or bush baby is another African primate of this forest level. Smaller than its relative, the potto, and far more lively, the galago has suction pads on its hands and feet, and long hind legs that enable it to make standing leaps many times its own length. Huge ears, sensitive to all sounds of the forest, further help this defenseless little animal keep one jump ahead of its enemies. When it picks its way through the dense foliage, the galago folds its ears flat so they will not hinder it.

Among other middle-tier animals, the hyrax or tree bear stands out as the only ungulate, or hoofed animal which has adapted itself to life in the trees. Despite its nickname, the hyrax is not a bear but a relative of the animal group that includes the horse and the rhinoceros.

The animals of the middle tier, generally small and weak,

mostly remain hidden during the day, timidly emerging at night. Here, as in the topmost canopy, they move along familiar routes as they come forth from their homes in hollow trunks or tree crowns or tangles of lianas to feed. Ivan Sanderson, during his two-week stay in the forest canopy, looked down and saw these animals taking "recognized paths through the trees—along one liana to a giant tree bole, up it a short way, down by another vine onto a palm head, and so on. Night after night you can sit watching one of these routes and animals keep passing, but switch your observation only a few feet and you will never see anything moving."

The forest floor is the home of the biggest animals. Some, like the elephant and rhinoceros, are confined to that zone, browsing on foliage and wandering in and out of the jungle as it pleases them. Others, such as the big cats, are at home at any level of the forest, following their prey into the highest trees.

The jaguar is the monarch of the South American forests. Massive, big-headed, short of tail, decked with circlets of dark spots, it slinks silently through the jungle glades, hunting smaller animals and sometimes willing to attack even man. In the forests of Africa the jaguar's role is played by the leopard, which skulks in low trees to pounce. The serval, a smaller jungle cat of Africa, is another fierce hunter. In the highest canopy roams the sleek, long, big-tailed genet, a swift and efficient killer that moves along the branches with the smoothness of flowing water. Tigers, which are native only to Asia, are frequently found in tropical forests but do not seem at home there; their weight makes them poor climbers, and they avoid the depths of the rain forest, remaining on its outskirts. Africa's great cat, the lion, is also too bulky for forest life.

Hoofed animals make up much of the population of the forest floor. The tapir of South and Central America and some parts of Asia is the biggest of these, an odd beast with the physique of a rhinoceros, the skin of a pig, and a drooping snout, four or five inches long, that looks like the beginning of an elephant's trunk. Tapirs are hermitlike, slow-witted animals that wander slowly through the forests, nibbling on leaves and green shoots. In South America, tapir meat is considered a delicacy.

The peccary, or wild pig, travels in packs of ten or twenty in South America, grubbing up roots, worms, insects, fallen fruits, lizards, snakes, and anything else that may be edible and easily obtained. Sometimes bands of several hundred peccaries run together. They are fierce animals whose sharp hooves and long tusks can do great damage. Jaguars, which feed on peccaries, have often been surrounded and trampled to death by them. The Indians, who are fond of peccary meat, avoid them in the forests and try to attack them while they are crossing a stream and are relatively helpless. Many a hunter has been driven up a tree by peccaries and kept there for hours. Other species of wild pigs, some of them huge and savage, are found in Africa and Asia.

As dainty as the pigs are coarse are the forest deer. The duiker, an antelope of Africa, shows the adaptations necessary for forest life. On the open plains, antelopes are powerful, fast-moving animals with long legs and necks, prominent horns, and big bodies. They are ideally designed for an environment in which one must be able to see enemies at a great distance and be ready for swift flight or vigorous defense. In the jungle, however, it is more desirable to be delicate of form, in order to slip easily through the tangled growth. Legs and necks are shorter, bodies are streamlined, horns are greatly reduced in size. The agile duiker could never outrun a leopard—as an antelope of the plains might do—but it can elude one by darting through the thickest underbrush.

The forest antelopes, like most forest creatures, are solitary animals. If they moved as a herd, as they do outside the jungle, the noise would invite every hungry leopard to attack. Such little

animals as the brockets and marsh deer of South America, the
munjacs of Asia, the duikers and water chevrotains of Africa,
pick their way cautiously and in solitude through the forests,
feeding on fallen fruits and plants, ears and nostrils ever alert
for danger.

The secluded forest world permits many animals to survive
that have long since become extinct outside. The tree sloth is one
such "living fossil" of the forest. Another is the anteater, a long-
snouted, bushy-tailed creature of South and Central America. This
odd-looking beast belongs to an ancient group that died out long
ago elsewhere. It prowls the forest floor in search of the tall nests
of ants and termites. With its sharp claws it rips a hole in the nest
and thrusts its long, sticky tongue inside. The ants march across
the anteater's tongue and abruptly find themselves being swallowed.

In the heart of the Congo forest lives the okapi, a short-necked
cousin of the giraffe. In the nineteenth century scientists discovered fossil bones that proved that giraffes had evolved from
such a short-necked form, millions of years ago. Then, to everyone's surprise, in 1900 the okapi came to light, almost identical
to the giraffe's fossil ancestor. It had survived because its remote
rain-forest home put it beyond the reach of hunters. Sir Harry
Johnston, the okapi's discoverer, wrote that "the atmosphere of
the forest was almost unbreathable with its Turkish-bath heat, its
reeking moisture, and its powerful smell of decaying, rotting
vegetation." He called it "a climate scarcely suitable for the
modern type of real humanity"—but the okapi thought it was
fine.

The lower depths of the forest shelter a number of birds that
have almost lost the use of their wings. In Africa, there are the
touracos and francolins, which escape enemies by running, not
by flying. Among the comparable South American birds is the
houtou, which Charles Waterton said could be seen "sitting in the

underwood, about a couple of yards from the ground. He lives on insects and the berries amongst the underwood, and very rarely is seen in the lofty trees." Though living in the forest's gloomiest zone, the houtou is elegant of hue. According to Waterton, its "whole body is green, with a bluish cast in the wings and tail; his crown, which he erects at pleasure, consists of black in the center, surrounded with lovely blue of two different shades: he has a triangular black spot, edged with blue, behind the eye extending to the ear; and on his breast a sable tuft, consisting of nine feathers edged also with blue."

The rain forest is thought to be the abode of serpents. This, like most common beliefs about rain forests, is an error. The forest has its snakes, on all levels, but snakes are much more widely seen outside the jungle than within.

Through the treetops move the poisonous arboreal snakes, such as the green mamba (*Dendraspis viridis*). This silent hunter wriggles along the branches, invisible against the green leafy backdrop, and strikes suddenly and fatally. Its chief prey is small birds; occasionally it gets a squirrel or a lizard.

There are relatively few poisonous snakes in the rain forest. Of 2400 species of snakes known in the world, fewer than two hundred are dangerous to man, and many of these are snakes of the deserts and plains. Of course, a snake does not have to be poisonous to be dangerous. The world's two giant snakes—the anaconda of South America and the python of Asia—are without poison, and kill by constriction, wrapping themselves about their prey and squeezing with fatal force. Anacondas more than thirty feet in length have been seen in South America, and the longest recorded python stretched thirty-three feet. Such snakes are large enough to kill almost any forest animal, though they may have trouble swallowing their victims afterward. Charles Waterton told of a twenty-two-foot anaconda that had swallowed a deer; it had engulfed everything but the head and antlers, and was waiting for its digestive processes to finish their work before going on with its meal.

The boa constrictor is the second largest South American snake. It rarely grows past a dozen feet in length, making it a poor second to the anaconda. Its killing habits are the same.

Most of the snakes a rain-forest visitor sees—if he sees any—are likely to be less ferocious. Many forest dwellers are sluggish burrowers that live in holes in the ground, coming forth to hunt at rare intervals. Others hide in the underbrush, slithering away at the first sign of human intruders. The poisonous snakes are generally nighttime hunters.

The rain forest by day, then, seems to be almost entirely a world of plants and trees and insects. Only occasionally will one see a large animal—perhaps a tapir crashing through the underbrush in South America or an elephant in the Orient. More likely the animal life that is encountered will be small, shy, and quick to disappear—a lizard, a small monkey, a bird.

Yet all about in the lush jungle living things are hidden. They lurk in the canopy's sky-high pathways, in the twisting cablework of lianas, in the hollow trunks of towering trees. The forest rustles with an unseen population, and wherever the stranger goes, he is followed by the staring gaze of hundreds of eyes.

7

Explorers of the
Rain Forest

What we think of as Western civilization—that is, our brand of civilization—is a northern affair. It was founded in Greece and Rome, neither of them tropical countries, and was nurtured in such cool-weather places as England, France, Germany, and Spain. Even if we trace the roots of our civilization back to ancient Egypt and Mesopotamia, they lie in hot, dry countries, not in hot, wet ones.

So the world of the rain forest is something alien to our heritage. We came to it as strangers, outsiders, discoverers. We looked upon its fantastic fertility as something bizarre and astounding. Of course, the rain forest had been "discovered" thousands of years ago by the people of tropical lands, and they saw nothing remarkable in it, for they were used to it. But in our rather self-centered way, we do not regard a place as properly discovered until Europeans or North Americans have done the discovering.

We do not know who was the first European to venture into the rain forests. The first of whom we have any information is Megasthenes, a Greek from Asia Minor. Seleucus, the ruler of

Persia, sent Megasthenes as an ambassador to the court of the Indian King Chandragupta in 302 B.C.

The ambassador was a man of consuming curiosity. During his stay in India, Megasthenes traveled and brought back a mass of information that was the foundation for all that the later Greeks knew of India. His own writings have been lost, but extracts from them were quoted by Greek geographers whose works survive. Megasthenes was struck by the vastness of India; he said there were 118 Indian nations and tribes in all, and described some of their major cities. He wrote of the River Ganges, which he said was ten miles across at its narrowest point (an exaggeration), and he told of Chandragupta's nine thousand elephants (probably the truth).

He has particularly vivid as an observer of nature. He spoke with wonder of the size and ferocity of the tigers and giant pythons, and wrote in awe about peacocks and parrots and monkeys. He described the huge trees of the Indian forests, the sprawling banyans and thick-stemmed bamboo. He brought back plenty of fantasy, too: winged serpents, winged scorpions, men with a single eye in the center of their foreheads, pygmies and giants, men with feet turned backward, heels in front, and many another startling wonder. Megasthenes had a keen imagination, but there can be no doubt that he really saw a tropical forest.

Contact between Europeans and the tropics was sparse after that. The Romans occupied North Africa but never went south of Egypt. Men solemnly decided that it was dangerous to go too far from Europe; voyagers to the south would enter a blazing realm of intolerable heat, those who went west would fall off the edge of the earth. For more than a thousand years the world was an unknown place to the men of Europe.

In the thirteenth century, a few men began to travel eastward across all of Asia to reach the court of China. The most famous of them was Marco Polo, who reached China in 1275 after his father and uncle had preceded him. Marco enrolled in the service of Kublai Khan, the Mongolian-born Emperor of China, and traveled through Kublai's vast domains. Marco went as far south as the northern frontier of Burma, getting a taste of the steaming tropics.

After Marco Polo's day, a veil of fear and superstition fell over Europe once more, and two centuries passed before any further exploration took place. Prince Henry of Portugal, surnamed "the Navigator," began sending expeditions down Africa's western coast early in the fifteenth century. Each year the Portuguese caravels dared to go a little farther to the south, until they crossed the equator without discovering the dreaded zone of fire. In 1488 the Portuguese reached the Cape of Good Hope, Africa's southern tip, and nine years later Vasco da Gama rounded the Cape and sailed to India. That opened Portuguese trade routes to the Orient, the land of spices and precious gems.

The early Portuguese seamen never penetrated deep enough into Africa's interior to find the rain forests. The first who did were four sailors who called on Mani, the black King of the Congo, in 1484. Their captain, Diego Cao, sent them inland as ambassadors. They traveled up the Congo for hundreds of miles, until they were in the midst of Africa's greatest forest. They saw the giant trees, the tangled screen of lianas, the interwoven crowns of the canopy, above which tropical storms burst in terrible fury. After months at the royal court, they returned to the coast, bearing the Congo monarch's permission for Portuguese traders and missionaries to enter his land. For the next two hundred years the Portuguese maintained outposts in the heart of Africa; but they were businessmen and priests, not scientists, and they paid little attention to the scenery. With one exception, there would be no careful view of Africa's forest world until the nineteenth century.

The exception was Andrew Battell, no scientist either, but

simply an English pirate captured by the Portuguese in 1589, while he was raiding the coast of Brazil. Battell was shipped over to Africa and imprisoned at the Portuguese colony of Angola. The Portuguese governor offered him his freedom if he would serve for some years as a trader, and he saw a good deal of Africa in the service of the Portuguese. He made several attempts to escape, was captured by the natives and imprisoned by them for two years, returned to Portuguese service, and finally gained his freedom and returned to England after an absence of some twenty years.

During his long and strange adventure, Battell saw the Congo forest and left a good description of it: "All woods and groves, so overgrown that a man may travel twenty days in the shadow, without any sun or heat. Here is no kind of corn nor grain, so that the people liveth only upon plantains [a type of banana] and roots of sundry other sorts, very good, and nuts; nor any kind of tame cattle, nor hens. But they have great store of elephants' flesh, which they greatly esteem, and many kinds of wild beasts."

Battell's short account of his travels, dictated after his return to England, also includes the first known description of the gorilla, which Battell called by its native name, *pongo*. "This *pongo* is in all proportions like a man," he said, "but that he is more like a giant in stature than a man; for he is very tall, and hath a man's face, hollow-eyed, with long hair upon his brows. His face and ears are without hair, and his hands also. His body is full of hair, but not very thick, and it is of a dunnish color. He differeth not from a man but in his legs, for they have no calf. He goeth always upon his legs, and carryeth his hands clasped upon the nape of his neck when he goeth upon the ground. They sleep in the trees, and build shelters from the rain. They feed upon fruit they find in the woods and upon nuts, for they eat no kind of flesh. They cannot speak, and have no more understanding than a beast."

This is a mixture of truth and falsehood, for gorillas are shorter in stature than men, and lean their hands on the ground when they walk. Despite these and other errors, Battell's description seems clearly to be that of a gorilla. However, it was another two hundred years before Europeans were willing to believe that such animals actually existed.

The era of scientific exploration of Africa began in 1788, when a dozen London gentlemen, lamenting the lack of knowledge about the "dark continent," founded the Association for Promoting the Discovery of the Inland Parts of the Continent of Africa. They financed an expedition to the Niger River, which was known to the Arabs of North Africa and which seemed to be a route to the interior.

The first two explorers sent out were killed on the way. The third gave up almost as soon as he started. The fourth, a tall, courageous Scot named Mungo Park, went off from Africa's western coast and made his way through hostile country to the fabled city of Timbuktu, and then to the Niger. He came back to England in 1797, after he had been thought dead, and wrote a book on his adventures that got all England excited about the exploration of Africa.

Park returned to Africa in 1805 with a much larger expedition. Its goal was to navigate the full length of the Niger and discover whether it connected to that great river of central Africa, the Congo, or flowed into the sea. Park died on the voyage, and not until 1896 was it discovered that the Niger flows southward to the sea without coming near the Congo. But this romantic explorer served as a symbol for an entire century of British travelers in Africa. Most of them, like Mungo Park himself, never entered the rain-forest zone. Their chief goal was to solve a centuries-old mystery by finding the source of the Nile, which John Speke and Richard Burton traced to Lake Victoria in 1856–59.

During those same years a young Frenchman was penetrating the dark heart of the continent for the first time since Andrew Battell's day. Paul du Chaillu, born about 1831 and raised in West Africa, was the son of a French merchant. He longed to know more about the mysterious jungles that lay east of the coastal settlement where he lived. When his family offered no encouragement to his plans he came to America, at the age of twenty-one, and persuaded a scientific organization in Philadelphia to underwrite a four-year expedition.

Between 1855 and 1859 du Chaillu covered eight thousand miles of inland territory, wandering the unknown forests and collecting mammals and birds. In 1861 he published his book, *Explorations and Adventures in Equatorial Africa*, in which he told of pygmies, cannibals, and gorillas. Du Chaillu was fiercely attacked by skeptical armchair travelers who, though they had never been to Africa themselves, refused to believe in tiny human beings and great shaggy apes. Only when du Chaillu produced a gorilla that he had shot himself did the loud and angry accusations of fraud die away.

During the next twenty years, equatorial Africa filled with Europeans of all sorts. Some were scientists who had come to study the strange jungle world. Some were adventurers looking for—and finding—their fortunes. Some, like Dr. David Livingstone, were missionaries spreading the word of Christianity. It was Dr. Livingstone's famous disappearance near Lake Tanganyika in 1868 that sent Henry Stanley, the twenty-seven-year-old star reporter of the New York *Herald*, to Africa.

Stanley was covering a civil war in Spain in 1869 when his publisher gave him a two-word assignment: "Find Livingstone." The newspaper was in no hurry; on his way to Africa, Stanley was ordered to cover the opening of the Suez Canal, attend various other events in Egypt, and make stops in Jerusalem, Constantinople, Russia, Persia, India, and just about every place else where something newsworthy was happening. Not until January, 1871, did he reach Zanzibar, just off Africa's eastern coast. Livingstone had not been heard from in nearly three years.

Four months later Stanley found the missionary, alive and well, at Ujiji on the eastern shore of Lake Tanganyika. Livingstone had been too busy to send word to anyone in the outside world, but he was in no need of rescuing.

"I did not know how he would receive me," Stanley wrote. "So I did what moral cowardice and false pride suggested was the best thing—walked deliberately to him, took off my hat and said:

" 'Dr. Livingstone, I presume?'

" 'Yes,' said he, with a kind smile, lifting his cap slightly.' "

Stanley spent four months traveling with Livingstone. His fame as an African explorer was made. When Livingstone died in 1873, Stanley appointed himself "Livingstone's heir" and talked the London *Daily Telegraph* and the New York *Herald* into paying the cost of a new expedition "to solve, if possible, the remaining problems of Central Africa; and to investigate and report upon the haunts of the slave traders."

The expedition consisted of Stanley, four other white men, and hundreds of native porters. Two of the Europeans died soon after the party left Zanzibar in November, 1874. After a march of 104 days, Stanley reached Lake Victoria and spent fifty-eight days circumnavigating this inland sea, twice the size of Belgium. Then he went on to do the same, in fifty-one days, for huge Lake Tanganyika, after which, in 1877, he followed the Lualaba River to the Congo River and the dense jungles that surround it. By August of that year, 999 days after he had set out, he returned to Zanzibar. His book, *Through the Dark Continent,* was an exciting description of his African adventures.

Stanley's third African expedition, which began in 1887, took him through the Congo rain forest once again. It was a troublesome journey, and in his account of it Stanley does not conceal his irritation with the discomforts of jungle travel. "Nothing but miles and miles, endless miles of forest," he wrote, "in various stages of growth and various degrees of altitude. . . ." He told how the marchers "passed through a wilderness of creeks, mud, thick scum-faced quagmires green with duckweed into which we sank knee-deep." Out of this they came into a dark forest where the "tossing of branches and groaning of mighty trees warned us of the approach of a tempest. . . . The rain was cold and heavily dripped, and every drop, large as a dollar on their cotton clothes, sent a shiver through the men." The jungle came to seem a "region of horrors" to Stanley. "I found it difficult to accustom myself to its gloom and its pallid solitude," he wrote.

For all that, Stanley could not help responding to the magnificence of the forest, and his descriptions tingle with the excitement he must have felt. "Lean but your hand on a tree, measure but your length on the ground, seat yourself on a fallen branch," he wrote, "and you will then understand what venom, fury, voracity, and activity breathes around you. Open your notebook, the page attracts a dozen butterflies, a honeybee hovers over your hand; other forms of bees dash for your eyes; a wasp buzzes in your ears, a huge hornet menaces your face, an army of pismires [ants] come marching to your feet. Some are already crawling up, and will presently be digging their scissor-like mandibles in your neck. Woe! Woe! And yet it is all beautiful—but there must be no sitting or lying down on this seething earth. It is not like your pine groves and your dainty woods in England. It is a tropic world, and to enjoy it you must keep slowly moving."

Stanley asked his readers of 1890 to imagine an area as big as all of France and Spain "closely packed with trees varying from 20 to 180 feet high, whose crowns of foliage interlace and prevent any view of the sky"—so huge was the rain forest. (He did not use that term, for it was not to be coined for another eight years.) He spoke of the lianas, like cables two to fifteen inches in diameter, folding around the trees like "endless anacondas." He wrote of the dangling tassels that were the roots of epiphytes, telling how "on every fork and on every horizontal branch" were "cabbage-like lichens of the largest kind, and broad spear-leaved plants, and orchids and clusters of vegetable marvels, and a drapery of delicate ferns. . . . Now cover tree, branch, twig, and creeper with a thick moss like a green fur," and the picture was complete.

Stanley told of the decaying carpet of rotting twigs, leaves, and branches, and here and there a gigantic fallen tree, its wood turning quickly to pulp. He described the forest light, "a magic dust perpetually shifting and playing, profound spaces of darkness relieved by the breadth of gray tree trunk, silvered rods of parasites, or fancy gray filigree of vine stems." Like all who enter the forest, Stanley returned again and again to the lianas, "winding in and out by mazy galleries of dark shadows, and emerging triumphant far above to lean their weight on branches, running coils at one place, forming loops at another place, and then stretching loosely their interminable lengths out of sight."

Stanley was perhaps the last great nineteenth-century explorer of Africa. By the time he died, in 1904, the entire continent had been taken over by European countries, and the colonial administrators of the new empires had extended their authority to the darkest depths of the jungle. But the forest world has not given up all its secrets in Africa, even today.

The rain forests of the New World have not lacked for explorers since the time of Columbus. On his first voyage, Columbus saw and marveled at the thick jungles of the West Indian islands. But greater wonders were ahead; early in the sixteenth century, Spanish and Portuguese explorers entered the much larger forests of South America.

The first Europeans to reach South America merely nibbled

at the edges of the continent, planting settlements along the north shore in what are now Venezuela and Colombia, poking cautiously into the mouth of the Amazon on the eastern shore, and conquering Peru, the golden kingdom of the western coast, cut off from the tropical lowlands by the Andes. But by 1535 a full-scale exploration of the interior was under way. The futile quest for El Dorado, a mythical city of fabulous wealth, brought Spaniards into the hot country just on the east side of the Andes. They pursued El Dorado eastward across the continent through ever thicker jungles. In the process, the mighty Amazon River was discovered, a river that carries as much water to the sea as a hundred Congos or nearly a thousand Mississippis. In the north, another jungle river, the Orinoco, was explored. The quest for El Dorado reached its climax in 1597, when Sir Walter Raleigh looked in vain for the glittering city in the forests of Guyana. After that, men lost interest in the search, which had cost many lives and made no one wealthy. Its chief result was the discovery of river routes through much of northern South America.

The first scientific explorer of the South American jungle—in fact, probably the first man who ever studied any jungle systematically—was Charles Marie de la Condamine of France. He was an aristocrat in the prerevolutionary France of Louis XV. When he was eighteen, in 1719, he met a Spanish officer who had been in America and caught from him the fever of exploration. But first came eleven years of study. La Condamine specialized in mathematics and geography and, when he was twenty-nine, was honored by election to the French Academy of Sciences.

The French Academy then was deeply involved in a controversy over the shape of the earth. Was it really round, or was it flat at the poles? The best way to find out was to send one expedition to the Arctic, a second to the equator, to measure the curvature of the planet. La Condamine was placed in charge of the expedition to the equator. He sailed from France in 1735, accompanied by ten fellow scientists.

During the next nine years La Condamine carried out a difficult and complicated series of measurements along the equator in Ecuador, whose name is Spanish for "equator." His results, along with those made in the far north, showed that the world indeed is slightly flattened at the poles. When the job was done, La Condamine decided to make the first part of his homeward journey a river voyage down the Amazon, all the way across South America to the Atlantic.

The trip took two months. As La Condamine was whisked down the rapid river, he measured the current, the width and depth of the water, and went ashore occasionally to study the jungle. He examined the trees and the vines and pointed out the relationships of the various kinds of living things in the forest, noticing the way the lianas bind the trees into a tight canopy. He collected samples of rubber from the natives and was shown the wild rubber trees. He made a waterproof rubber covering for his scientific instruments.

No one had ever looked at a jungle with such discerning eyes before. In 1745 La Condamine wrote his *A Voyage Through the Inner Parts of South America*, which was translated into several languages and inspired a number of later expeditions.

A young man who read La Condamine's book and developed a taste for tropical exploration was Alexander von Humboldt, who was born in Prussia in 1769. Humboldt decided as a youth to devote his life to science, and succeeded in mastering every science from botany and zoology to geology and physics in a way that has never been equaled. In 1797, when he inherited his parents' wealth, he left Germany with the intention of traveling and studying all over the world.

In Paris the twenty-eight-year-old Humboldt met a botanist named Aimé Bonpland. They planned an expedition to Egypt, but difficulties arose, and instead they went to Madrid, where Humboldt wangled an interview with the King of Spain. The young scientist persuaded the monarch to let him make a survey of the Spanish empire in South America, which no foreign traveler had been permitted to tour since La Condamine, fifty years earlier. The King supplied Humboldt and Bonpland with royal letters of recommendation, guaranteeing them a good welcome wherever they went.

They sailed for the New World in June, 1799. On July 16, they landed in Venezuela, and the next day Humboldt ecstatically described his first impressions of the tropics in a letter to his brother:

"We are here in a divine country. Wonderful plants; electric eels, tigers [he meant jaguars], armadilloes, monkeys, parrots; and many, many, real, half-savage Indians, a handsome and interesting race. . . . What trees! Coconut trees, 50 to 60 feet high; *Poinciana pulcherrima* with a foot high bouquet of magnificent, bright-red flowers; pisang and a host of trees with enormous leaves and scented flowers, as big as the palm of a hand, of which we knew nothing. . . . And what colors in birds, fish, even crayfish (sky blue and yellow)! We rush around like the demented; we pick up one object to throw it away for the next. Bonpland keeps telling me that he will go mad if the wonders do not cease soon."

They had not yet seen a real rain forest. They spent eighteen months in Venezuela, making astronomical observations, experiencing an earthquake, and experimenting with electric eels. Heading inland from the Venezuelan coast in a southwesterly direction, they passed through grassy plains stretching for hundreds of miles, and in March, 1800, entered the dense rain forests of the Orinoco basin.

A large sailing canoe with four Indian oarsmen and a pilot was their home for many months. When it rained, they huddled in a cabin near the stern, under a roof of leaves; Humboldt made his scientific observations on a table of oxhides stretched over wooden frames; at night, they camped in hammocks beside the Orinoco, lighting fires to keep the jaguars away. As they went along, the cages of monkeys and birds they collected began to take up so much room in the canoe that there scarcely was room for the passengers. For food, they had rice, bananas, fried ants, and now and then a fried monkey. In the deepest and most dense part of the forest, they were unable to see the sun or stars for twelve days because of the steady rain; this greatly hampered Humboldt's astronomical observations.

The customary shape of rain-forest trees made it hard for them to carry on botanical observation either. "All these trees," wrote Humboldt, "were more than one hundred or one hundred and ten feet high. As their trunks throw out branches only toward the summit, we had some trouble in procuring both leaves and flowers. The latter were frequently strewed upon the ground at the foot of the trees; but, the plants of different families being grouped together in these forests, and every tree being covered with lianas, we could not, with any degree of confidence, rely on the authority of the natives, when they assured us that a flower belonged to such or such a tree."

After the Orinoco journey, the explorers went westward to Colombia, and then on to Mexico and Cuba. The spring of 1804 saw them in Philadelphia, and by the summer their ship docked in France. Humboldt published a lengthy book, *Personal Narrative of Travels to the Equinoctial Regions of America*, rich in descriptions of the plant and animal life he saw. Humboldt's book overflows with accounts of howler monkeys, eels, man-eating fish, turtles, giant rodents, huge trees, enormous lianas. Despite his dry, overly scientific style, his account of his voyages makes irresistible reading.

In Humboldt's footsteps came a succession of tireless naturalists who plunged enthusiastically into the wilds of South America. One of the first was Charles Waterton, born in 1782, who made four journeys through the tropics between 1812 and 1825. Neither disease nor fatigue slowed Waterton. In his book, *Wanderings in South America,* he extolled jungle life and invited his readers to join him. "So matted and interwoven are the tops of the trees above you," he wrote, "that the sun is not felt once all the way, saving where the space which a newly fallen tree occupied lets in his rays upon you. The forest contains an abundance of wild hogs, lobbas, acouries, powisses, maams, maroudis, and waracabas, for your nourishment, and there are plenty of leaves to cover a shed, whenever you are inclined to sleep.... Traveller, forget for a little while the idea thou hast of wandering farther on, and stop and look at this grand picture of vegetable nature!"

Waterton was a sharp-eyed observer who recorded accurate descriptions of the rain forest (a liana called the bush-rope, he said, was "nearly as thick as a man's body, twisted like a corkscrew round the tallest trees, and rearing its head above their tops") and its inhabitants (his account of the tree sloth was the first reliable one). His quaintly written book offers some views of North America, too; he visited New York City in 1824 and expressed rapturous admiration for Broadway which he thought the finest street in any city of the world: "There are no steam-engines to annoy you by filling the atmosphere full of soot and smoke; the houses have a stately appearance; while the eye is relieved from the perpetual sameness . . . by lofty and luxuriant trees."

From Humboldt's Prussian homeland came the brothers Robert and Richard Schomburgk. Robert, the elder, carried out a botanical exploration of what was then British Guiana in 1835, when he was thirty-one years old, at the request of the Royal Geographical Society of London. Six years later, he returned to determine the boundary between British Guiana and Venezuela, and this time took along his brother Richard, seven years his junior.

Robert Schomburgk measured his boundary—it was called the Schomburgk line for many years—and brought back to London a variety of tropical plants, including a magnificent water lily which he named *Victoria regis*, after Great Britain's young new Queen. Richard, who fell ill of yellow fever almost as soon as he reached South America, recovered and spent three years in the interior, returning with much valuable information about the previously unexplored forest.

The first naturalist from the United States to explore South America was William H. Edwards, who spent eight months in 1846 collecting animals along the Amazon. There was nothing out of the ordinary about his brief journey, and his book, *A Voyage up the River Amazon*, is no classic of adventure. But Edwards is an important figure if only because he served as the direct inspiration for two of the most celebrated of tropical explorers, Alfred Russel Wallace and Henry Walter Bates.

When Edwards' book was published in 1847, Wallace was an English schoolteacher of twenty-four, Bates the twenty-two-year-old son of a successful businessman. Wallace was interested in plants, Bates in insects. Their common love for natural history had drawn them together in 1844. For several years they talked of making a scientific journey to some remote place but never quite could choose one in particular. Their plans were the half-serious ones of young men unsure of themselves. Then came Edwards' book, which Wallace said in later years "was so clearly and brightly written, described so well the beauty and the grandeur of tropical vegetation . . . that Bates and myself at once agreed that this was the very place for us to go."

By coincidence, Edwards happened to be in London at that time. Wallace and Bates sought him out and received from him some first-hand hints about South American exploration. By the end of May, 1848, the two young naturalists were in Brazil.

They made their headquarters at the coastal town of Pará (now called Belém) for nearly two years, going on excursions together, growing accustomed to the tropical climate, and learning the local language, Portuguese. Then they separated. Bates remained close to Pará, while Wallace went inland to the town of Manaus, where the Amazon is joined by its great tributary, the Rio Negro.

During 1850 Wallace traveled up the Rio Negro, a river

Alfred Russel Wallace

named for the black color of its waters, and in February, 1851, reached the Venezuelan town of San Carlos. He explored the region of the Orinoco basin and despite the steady downpour of heavy rain was able to gather many animal specimens new to science. He collected forty species of butterflies, including the brilliant blue *Morpho*. Then he retraced his path to Manaus to store his collections and assemble supplies for another river journey.

This time Wallace went up the Rio Negro to one of its tributaries, the Uaupés River, traveling westward along the equator for many miles. From time to time he left the river and entered the dense rain forest, in which he felt quite at home. The mighty forest trees "produce feelings in the beholder of admiration and awe," he wrote. Despite the difficulties of the work, he collected specimens of plant and animal life and became an admiring student of the jungle Indians. Late in his life, Wallace wrote that he remembered three features in particular of his South American journey:

"The first was the virgin forest, everywhere grand, often beautiful and sublime; the second, the wonderful variety and exquisite beauty of the butterflies and birds; and the third, the meeting and living with man in a state of nature—with absolutely uncontaminated savages. The true denizen of the Amazonian forest, like the forest itself, is unique and not to be forgotten."

After a few weeks of travel on this second expedition up the Rio Negro, Wallace came down with that bane of jungle travelers, malaria. Fits of fever, perspiration, and shaking attacked him every day or two. He settled at the small town of São Joaquim, where the Uaupés joins the Negro, and, he writes, "I remained till the beginning of February, the ague continuing, but with diminished force; and though with an increasing appetite and eating heartily, yet gaining so little strength, that I could with difficulty stand alone, or walk across the room with the assistance of two sticks." He grew so yellow and wasted by the disease that he seemed to be dying.

Then, early in 1852, Wallace returned to his boat, although he was not yet fully recovered. He pushed on into the west, entering what is now Colombia. The effects of the struggle with malaria so weakened him that he had to give up at that point and return to Manaus. In July, 1852, he sailed from Pará for England.

Seven hundred miles east of Bermuda, the ship on which he was a passenger caught fire and went down, taking to the bottom the priceless specimens Wallace had collected. The passengers escaped in open boats and spent ten days on the high seas trying to reach Bermuda. Drinking water and food were almost exhausted, and Bermuda still two hundred miles away, when Wallace and the other survivors were picked up by another ship. He returned to England, weary from his jungle experiences and from the shipwreck and saddened by the loss of his collections. Yet almost as soon as his strength came back, Wallace headed to the Orient for new adventures.

His friend Henry Bates, meanwhile, had remained close to his headquarters at Pará. Though he made a number of side journeys and one lengthy inland trip, he found enough right at hand on the coast to occupy him. "I wished to explore districts at my ease," he wrote later, and in his eleven years on the Amazon he covered just three regions: Pará, near the mouth of the great river; Santarém, a few hundred miles upstream; and Ega, fourteen hundred miles from the coast.

He covered them in detail, though. Between 1848 and 1859, Bates collected fourteen thousand species of insects, fifty-two species of mammals, 360 of birds, 140 of reptiles, 120 of fishes, and thirty-five of mollusks. That was an average rate of nearly four species collected a day. He believed that eight thousand of these species were new to science.

Bates was a tireless scientist whose keen eyes searched everywhere. Insects were his main interest, of course, but he made extensive investigations of toucans, marmosets, turtles, spider monkeys, and other animals, as well as carrying out a study of the customs of the native Indian tribes. In his first few years, spent at Pará, Bates made pioneering studies of leaf-cutter ants. He was the first to discover that the ants did not eat the leaves they collected, although he was wrong about the use he thought they put them to, saying that the leaves were used "to thatch the domes which cover the entrances to their subterranean dwellings, thereby protecting from the deluging rains the young broods in the nests beneath." A later naturalist, Thomas Belt, discovered the existence of the fungi that digest the leaves brought them by the ants.

Bates also devoted some time to the army ants, *Eciton*, and found a band of these grim warriors in a mood of relaxation. He wrote: "They seemed to have been all smitten with a sudden fit of laziness. Some were walking slowly about, others were brushing their antennae with their forefeet; but the drollest sight was their cleaning one another. Here and there an ant was seen stretching forth first one leg and then another, to be brushed or washed by one or more of its comrades, who performed the task by passing the limb between the jaws and the tongue, finishing by giving the antennae a friendly wipe ... the conclusion that the ants were engaged merely in play was irresistible."

Wasps, termites, beetles, moths, butterflies—for Bates, the insect harvest was incredible. He had never imagined that insect life could be so abundant, with hundreds of species in every small area. As he gradually moved deeper into the continent, he found so many new species that it was a day-and-night job to keep his collections in good order.

Not far from Pará he saw and observed such jungle dwellers as anteaters, sloths, boa constrictors, and monkeys. When he moved inland to Santarém, at the mouth of the Rio Tapajós, the countryside proved so interesting that he spent three and a half years there. At one town near Santarém butterflies were astoundingly common, and Bates made it his home for forty days, capturing three hundred butterfly species within a short distance from the village. When he felt he had done enough work in the vicinity of Santarém, Bates shifted his locale to Ega, an inland town that he had visited on a brief journey in 1850. His stay at Ega also lasted three and a half years. He collected some seven thousand species of insects there, including 550 species of butterflies.

During the last year of his stay at Ega, Bates' health finally began to give way. Like his friend Wallace, he came down with malaria and had to return to England, sailing from Pará in June, 1859. It was a sad parting, for he had hoped to spend the rest of his life in the tropics. He never went abroad again. His book *The Naturalist on the River Amazons*, published in 1863, is a lively classic of scientific adventure that still is widely read today.

A third British explorer, whose name is often bracketed with those of Wallace and Bates, is Richard Spruce. He came to South America in 1849, a year after the other two, and spent fifteen fruitful years in botanical research there. Born in 1817, Spruce was six years older than Wallace, eight years older than Bates, but it was the quick fame of these younger men that brought him to the tropics. He was a botanist by inclination, a schoolteacher by profession; when the school where he taught closed in 1844, Spruce made his hobby his livelihood. For two years he traveled through Europe, collecting specimens for sale to museums and private collectors. Then, hearing of the success of Bates and Wallace, Spruce persuaded eleven collectors to finance his own South American expedition.

Soon after his arrival in Brazil, he met Wallace and Bates, and struck up a strong friendship. But on his exploring trips he generally traveled alone, though he made a few brief excursions with Bates. To the forest Indians, Spruce was an odd figure, extremely tall and lean, blue-eyed and brown-bearded. He often amused himself on the river by playing on his bagpipes, letting loose an eerie sound never heard before in the Amazon jungle.

Spruce's eleven sponsors expected him to enrich their collections of exotic plants, and he did not disappoint them. In his ten thousand miles of forest travel he collected and sent back to England thirty thousand different plants, all of them carefully mounted and labeled. Spruce took pains to find out the native name for each plant and the uses it might have. When the Indians told him a certain plant was good to eat or useful for medicine, Spruce tried to check their statements by sampling the plant himself.

In the process of gathering this information Spruce became fluent in twenty-one native languages and spent many pleasant hours talking with the Indians. He often tried to tell them about the world beyond their jungle. Once, he wrote, he "took some pains to describe the ocean to a lot of Indians, telling them of the immense extent and almost fathomless depth—how long it took to cross it, and how it had the Old World on one side of it and the New World on the other. They listened eagerly, giving vent to occasional grunts of admiration, and I thought them intelligent. When I had done, a venerable Indian turned to the rest and said in a tone of wonder and awe, 'It is the river of his land! What is this little river of ours' (pointing to the Amazon) 'compared to *that!*' "

Spruce understood the forest's structure of several levels more clearly than any earlier botanist. He saw the relationship between the big trees and the small ones, and lamented that he was unable to climb to the canopy for a close look. In his notes on his travels, he speaks of his disappointment "in not finding some agile and willing Indians to run like cats or monkeys up the tree for me . . . the only way to obtain the flowers and fruits was to cut down the tree." To Spruce it seemed like an act of vandalism to cut down a huge tree simply to study its leaves and flowers. But there was no other way, and he comforted himself with the thought that there were so many trees the jungle would not miss a few.

Like Bates and Wallace, Spruce had to leave his beloved jungle when his health broke. In 1864, ill with an intestinal disease, he left for England. In the remaining twenty-eight years of his life, his malady stayed with him, leaving him so feeble that he could walk only short distances and could not use a microscope more than a few minutes at a time. Yet in the first seven years after his return he was able to publish two technical books on Amazon vegetation. He never managed to write the popular book of his travels that could have made him as famous as Bates or Wallace. His later years were darkened by poverty; he lost his savings in a business failure, and lived on a pension of $250 a year obtained for him by fellow botanists. After his death, his notes and letters were gathered and edited for publication by his friend Alfred Wallace.

The pioneering age of South American rain-forest exploration ends with the German, Andreas F. W. Schimper, who helped to form much of modern scientific thinking about tropical jungles. Schimper traveled in the Orient as well as in tropical America, and in 1898 published an important book that was translated into English as *Plant-geography upon a Physical Basis*. In this book Schimper coined the term *Regenwald*, "rain forest," to describe the jungles of the tropics.

The third great rain-forest zone of the world, that of Asia, has had its share of explorers. Perhaps the first was the British diplomat, Sir Stamford Raffles. Born in 1781, Raffles became a clerk with the British East India Company at the age of fourteen and rapidly rose to prominence. The East India Company then ran Great Britain's Asian empire for its own profit. When he was twenty-four, Raffles was chosen to be assistant secretary to the company's new governor at the Malayan colony of Penang.

That began his career in Southeast Asia. He moved from one governmental post to another, often in hot water with his superiors because of his unorthodox ideas. He wanted Great Britain to expand its power in that part of the world, and his methods of empire building caused great controversy at home.

When not busy with political matters, Raffles studied the natural history of the tropics. Abdullah, his Malayan interpreter, wrote of Raffles that "he kept four persons on wages, each in their peculiar departments; one to go to the forests in search of various kinds of leaves, flowers, fungi, pulp, and such like products. Another he sent to collect all kinds of flies, grasshoppers, bees in all their varieties, as well as scorpions, centipedes, and such like, giving him needles as well as pins with a box to stick the creatures therein. Another he sent with a basket to seek for coral, shells, oysters, mussels, cockles, and such like; also fishes of various species; and another to collect animals, such as birds, jungle fowl, deer, stags, mouse-deers, and so forth. Then he had a large book with thick paper, whose use was for the keeping of the leaves and flowers. . . . He kept a barrel full of arrack, or brandy, and when he had got snakes, scorpions, centipedes, or such like, he would put them into it till they were dead, before putting them in bottles."

Transferred to Java, then to the neighboring island of Sumatra, Raffles explored tirelessly everywhere, accompanied by his wife. They visited a cannibal tribe, kept bears and tigers as pets and playmates for their children, and marched through rain forests. Raffles wrote of the grandeur of the forest: "The magnitude of the flowers, creepers and trees, contrasts strikingly with the stunted and, I had almost said, pygmy vegetation of England. Compared with our forest-trees, your largest oak is a mere dwarf. Here we have creepers and vines entwining larger trees, and hanging suspended for more than a hundred feet, in girth not less than a man's body, and many much thicker; the trees seldom under a hundred, and generally approaching a hundred and sixty to two hundred feet in height. One tree we measured was, in circumference, nine yards! and this is nothing to one I measured in Java. . . ."

On Sumatra, Raffles' home was a private zoo. He had two leopards as friendly as house cats, a bear that liked champagne, and such forest creatures as gibbons and siamangs. But his career in the Orient was cut short by disease, the usual fate of these British jungle explorers. Haggard and prematurely old from tropical fevers, Raffles at last agreed to return to England only after an epidemic took the lives of all but one of his children. His collections of plants and stuffed animals were carefully loaded aboard a ship bound for home. Also on board were the tame leopards, a rare tapir, and other live animals. The ship sailed on February 2, 1824; that evening, a fire broke out and the passengers escaped in boats, losing all their possessions. Raffles, heartbroken at the loss of his scientific collections, sailed home on another ship, only to find himself forced into bankruptcy through the failure of a banking house. He was only forty-five when he died in 1826, worn out by hardships and disease but assured of a permanent place in the story of tropical exploration.

As we have seen, Alfred Russel Wallace suffered a similar tragic loss of his scientific specimens in 1852, when homeward bound from South America. Like Raffles, he was fever-stricken and weary when he reached England. But he was not yet thirty years old, and he was able to rebound from disaster to begin a new career.

Wallace sailed for Malaya and explored some of the same jungles Raffles had visited. He remarked on how similar in appearance they were to the forests of South America; for rain forests are very much alike in tropical lowlands everywhere, though their individual species may differ. When Wallace heard some native Malayan helpers speaking Portuguese, he said, he thought he was back in Brazil. The main difference seemed to be that there were fewer butterflies in the Orient. But of course the actual trees were of different species there, as Wallace was in a better position to know than any other man.

He remained in tropical Asia until 1862, boldly entering the territory of headhunters and other wild tribes. He never felt in any danger. Frequently he lived alone in the heart of a jungle. He wrote to a friend, "You cannot perhaps imagine how I have come to love solitude. I seldom have a visitor but I wish him away in an hour. I find it very favorable to reflection."

At one jungle camp Wallace raised a baby orangutan, feeding it rice water from a nursing bottle and writing jokingly to friends about it as though it were his own child. ("Of course baby cannot walk yet, but I let it crawl about on the floor to exercise its limbs; but it is the most wonderful baby I ever saw. . . .") He collected insects as well as plants—in 1858 he sent his friend Bates a list of 8,540 species of insects he had gathered—and spent a good deal of time pondering the process whereby nature had produced so many different kinds of living things.

Wallace suffered from attacks of fever, "and every day during the cold and succeeding hot fits had to lie down for several hours, during which time I had nothing to do but to think over any subjects then particularly interesting me." In these periods of enforced idleness he came to see an explanation for the multitude of species. A given plant or animal, he suggested, underwent gradual change from generation to generation, until new species had evolved from the old ones. This process, according to Wallace, went on continuously, and thus many new species had originated.

He thought this idea over for a while. Then, in a house on the edge of the Borneo jungle, Wallace wrote a short paper called "On the Tendency of Varieties to Depart Indefinitely from the

Original Type," and mailed it to a naturalist in England whom he greatly admired, asking for comments.

The other naturalist's name was Charles Darwin. For fourteen years, Darwin had been mulling the same concept. He was still collecting evidence and had not published anything about his theory—the theory of evolution. Now, out of the distant jungles, came Wallace's paper with the same idea! "I never saw a more striking coincidence," Darwin wrote. "If Wallace had my own sketch, he could not have made a better short abstract."

On July 1, 1858, at a public scientific meeting, Darwin read his original paper of 1844 and a manuscript he had written in 1857, outlining his ideas on evolution. That proved that he had come upon the theory before receiving Wallace's letter. But he also gave Wallace full credit for the simultaneous discovery and read Wallace's paper at the same meeting. Darwin's name is forever linked to the theory of evolution, but Alfred Wallace must also be honored for his part in discovering it.

After he returned to England, Wallace wrote several scientific books and a popular account of his travels, *The Malay Archipelago*. He spent the rest of his long life in his native country and died in 1913, in his ninetieth year.

Today not a month goes by without a scientific expedition's entering some tropical forest. The modern explorers travel by jeep, keep in contact with the outside world by radio, and hop from place to place by helicopter. They carry an array of pills and drugs to protect them from tropical diseases. Things have changed quite a bit since the trailblazing days of Humboldt, Wallace, Raffles, du Chaillu, and the other bold men who penetrated the jungles of the tropics more than a century ago.

8

The Promise of the Rain Forest

In a world that has never had enough food for everyone, the rain forest seems to hold unlimited agricultural promise. Surely the jungles of the tropics, if properly cultivated, can be turned into farms that would yield rich benefits for mankind. Everything appears perfect. The growing season can last twelve months a year; there would never be any problem of irrigation; and certainly the jungle soil must be extraordinarily fertile. The wild, dense growth of the rain forest testifies to that.

The truth, though, is harsh and surprising. A rain forest can *not* be turned into a farmer's paradise overnight. Nearly every attempt to convert jungle into farmland has ended in dismal failure.

The main problem lies in the soil, which is not nearly as fertile as one might think. Soil is formed from rock, which slowly crumbles as it is exposed to weathering and to the chemical effects of certain forms of plant life. Over a period of millions of years, a bare rock face becomes covered with a thin coating of soil, just enough to permit larger plants to gain a foothold on it. This leads a further breakdown of the underlying rock until a deep layer of soil, thick enough to support forest growth, is formed.

In the tropics the soil tends to be made up of sand or clay. It is lacking in silica, potassium, calcium, phosphorous, carbon, and most of the other chemical nutrients important to the growth of plants. It is rich in the ores of iron or aluminum, which are not nourishing for plant life. There is little or no humus, the fertile, dark earth formed from decayed vegetation.

The reason is the heavy rainfall of the humid tropics. Plant nutrients dissolve easily in water; iron and aluminum ores do not. Day after day, the falling rain dissolves the all-important nutrients. Some of the valuable chemicals are washed downward into the lower levels of the soil, leaving the upper levels too poor for much plant growth. Other key nutrients are simply swept away by the rain water as it rushes across the land. The trickling water, carrying with it the vital chemicals of the soil, runs toward streams that become rivers and flow toward the sea.

Tropical soil thus is washed free of its most useful ingredients, a process known as leaching. The leached soil is much poorer than that of an Iowa cornfield or a Vermont forest. The rain forest's growth is lush despite, not because of, its soil. In the wet tropics, conditions of temperature and rainfall are so favorable that a forest will enjoy tremendous growth even on such poor soil.

Why, then, is it impossible to replace a rain forest with a farm?

The rain forest exists in a delicate balance of nature. There is an endless cycle of renewal. The roots of the giant trees go into the deeper levels of the soil—the layers to which the rains have washed the rich nutrients. In dissolved form, these nutrients rise through the roots to be used by the trees. Nourished by what they draw from the soil, the trees expand, adding new leaves and branches.

The leaves fall to the ground, along with twigs, flowers, and other debris. Everything immediately is attacked by the forces of decay—fungi, bacteria, termites, and such. In the steaming warmth, the fallen material rots quickly, and its nutrients are given back to the soil. The whole forest takes part in the cycle. The decaying bodies of forest animals and the rotting trunks of fallen trees add to the supply of nourishment in the soil. Some of the nutrients are scoured away by surface water, but most remain locked in the cycle, used in the forest vegetation over and over again.

Thus under the closed canopy of a rain forest the soil, while not very fertile to begin with, keeps the nutrients it does contain. Trouble begins when the forest is cut down and cleared away to make room for agriculture.

Now the bare topsoil is exposed to the full force of the tropical rains. In the forest, the dense upper levels of foliage break the fall of the drops so that only a gentle trickle reaches the ground. In a cleared patch, the raindrops skim the earth like a million tiny knives. The topsoil, which contains the nutrients released by decayed organic matter, is cut away and carried out to sea. The Amazon takes millions of pounds of soil into the Atlantic every year, lowering the land surface of its huge basin by a fraction of an inch.

The cycle of plant nutrients is broken. No longer is there a forest to cover the soil with fallen leaves and twigs. In a flash, the topsoil is eroded away, taking with it the forest's heritage of nourishment, and the remaining nutrients are pounded far into the earth by the rain.

Cultivated plants face terrible problems in such an environment. Their roots are too shallow to absorb the nutrients deep in the ground. The swollen ball of fire that is the tropical sun beats down with awful effect. Exposure to sunlight bakes the soil and further improverishes it. The organisms of decay living in the soil are killed by the heat. If a dry spell comes, the soil may turn to dust, to be blown away by the first good wind. Where a thick forest once stood, now is something very much like a desert.

In many parts of the tropics damage far more serious than leaching and erosion takes place when the forest is removed. A chemical reaction turns the soil to rock and destroys all hope of agriculture.

This is called laterization, and occurs where the soil is exceptionally rich in iron or aluminum. Laterization results from the combination of oxygen in the soil with the iron or aluminum to form iron oxide or aluminum oxide, the ores of those metals. In a rain forest, this lateritic soil is covered with a more nutritious topsoil formed by the decay of forest vegetation. When the rain forest goes, the topsoil often follows, exposing the lateritic layers beneath to the action of the sun.

Once the sun strikes this sort of soil, it begins to bake it into a kind of brick. This was the undoing of Iata, an agricultural colony set up some years ago by the Brazilian government in the heart of the Amazon forest. Bulldozers cleared the forest, and crops were planted. The seemingly fertile soil, with its covering of forest humus, swiftly weathered away. The sun went to work, transforming the iron-rich lateritic soil beneath to bricklike laterite, a solid rock. Within five years the cleared fields of Iata had become pavements of stone.

Other tropical countries, particularly in Africa, have experienced the transformation of soil into laterite when forests were cleared. Lateritic soil may have been the ruin of the only two great civilizations that ever flourished in a jungle environment—the Khmers of Cambodia and the Mayas of Central America.

The Khmers were the dominant people of Southeast Asia for six centuries. Their first great king, Jayavarman II, began construction of the capital city of Angkor Thom ("Great City") about A.D. 800. Each of his successors added to this jungle city until it was one of the wonders of the world. Between 1113 and

1150, King Suryavarman II constructed Angkor Thom's greatest building, the temple known as Angkor Wat. This magnificent edifice, with huge walls covered with lovely reliefs, was built of laterite—the reddish natural brick of the tropics.

In 1432, Angkor Thom was abandoned by its builders. We do not know why. Some historians believe that the grandiose building projects of the last great king, Jayavarman VII, so exhausted

Angkor Wat, Cambodia

the Khmers that they went into a decline brought on by fatigue and were an easy prey for enemies. More recently it has been suggested that what was exhausted was the fertility of the lateritic soil around Angkor Thom. Much of the Khmer farmland must have turned to laterite, and the rest simply was drained of richness and could no longer produce crops. The Khmers were compelled to seek other lands, and their fantastic city was swallowed by the jungle.

It remained forgotten until 1863, when Henri Mouhot, a French naturalist looking for butterflies, came through the Cambodian forest. He slashed away the vines and stepped into an open glade. And there, looming above the trees, were the five titanic towers of Angkor Thom, wrapped in the close embrace of lianas. Today, the banyans and vines have been cut back, the snakes and the bats have been evicted, and Angkor Thom looks much the way it did when it was the mighty city of the Khmers. But it is a lifeless city, a city for tourists.

The Mayas of Central America also were city builders. They built in limestone, not in laterite, and between A.D. 400 and 600 constructed many great cities in the jungles of what now are Honduras and Guatemala. Huge temples and towering pyramids indicate the skill of the Mayan architects. Beyond the cities were the cultivated fields.

Suddenly and mysteriously, the Mayas abandoned their great cities and moved northward out of Central America into Yucatán, the thumblike peninsula that juts out of eastern Mexico. Here, in a much drier climate, they erected new cities even mightier than the old ones, between A.D. 900 and 1460. The migrations of the Mayas probably were a result of the steady exhaustion of the soil. When their farms ceased to produce crops, there was no choice but to leave everything and start over in a new part of the country.

The Mayas practiced what we call slash-and-burn agriculture.

Slash-and-burn, also known as shifting agriculture, has many names in many parts of the world—*milpa* in tropical America, *kaingin* in Thailand, *ladang* in Malaya, *taunggya* in Burma. Whatever the name, the general principle is the same everywhere.

In slash-and-burn agriculture, a patch of forest is cleared by hacking away the shrubbery and low trees. The huge trees are left standing but are killed by cutting a ring around their trunks. The slashed trees are allowed to dry and then are burned. The living forest around the clearing rarely catches fire, because it is so damp.

The ashes are left on the ground. At the beginning of the rainy season, seeds are pushed into the surface soil with a sharpened planting stick. The warm weather and heavy rainfall do the rest. Crops such as corn, yams, bananas, cotton, or peanuts grow quickly. The native farmer keeps wild pigs, birds, and other intruders away from his field, and plucks the biggest weeds.

If he is lucky, he can farm the field for four or five years. More often, a single good season is all he gets. The rain leaches away the nutrients contained in the ashes and strips off the top-soil. The sun does its share of harm. Soon, the plot is drained of fertility, fit only for growing weeds. The farmer abandons it and slashes a new field elsewhere in the jungle.

While he is tending this field, he hopes that the abandoned field will return to fertility. Perhaps it will, if conditions are right. First come weeds so tough that they can thrive in the poor soil and can stand the exposure to sun, wind, and rain. Within a few weeks they form a thick cover of vegetation on the ground. As they die and decay, they enrich the soil, and shrubs and low trees take over. These are not rain-forest trees, but rather the sunshine-loving trees of the open country. They dominate the abandoned field for ten or fifteen years. By then, they are fifty or sixty feet high and form a closed canopy. Underneath, shade-loving forest trees can establish themselves, and eventually these become dominant, since the earlier tree population cannot re-plenish itself under the now-shady conditions. Within a century, a new rain forest will have appeared.

Of course, the slash-and-burn farmer cannot afford to wait a century. Limited as he is to the jungle surrounding his own vil-lage, he is forced to return to abandoned plots in ten years or less. Even then, the new growth will be enough to allow him an-other couple of seasons of farming, when he slashes and burns it to enrich the soil. However, if the same plot is burned too often, it will be invaded by thick grass that prevents the forest from returning. Where grass has come to occupy former forest land, any sort of agriculture, even slash-and-burn, becomes virtually impossible.

The life of the slash-and-burn farmer is therefore difficult. He can never be sure of getting more than one good year out of each ten or fifteen on any field. He must keep rotating his land, for-ever slashing one forest area while letting another lie fallow. Yet, despite its drawbacks, this kind of farming allows a small village group to provide for its own needs fairly well. Slash-and-burn farming is practiced by 250 million people—perhaps one person out of every twelve or fifteen in the world. For whole nations it is the chief bulwark against famine.

So long as this kind of farming is done in small pockets of the jungle, it causes no real harm. One village can thrive for cen-turies in the same part of a forest, moving in regular succession from field to field. The little areas of destroyed forest restore themselves in a generation or so, and the surrounding forest shields the cleared places from the worst effects of sun, wind, and rain.

But slash-and-burn agriculture cannot support a large popula-tion concentrated in one place. As the Khmers and Mayas found out, a city cannot survive that way. The expanding population surges outward until, instead of small pockets of cleared land, there are long continuous farm units. The larger the cleared area, the harsher the damage done by the weather. When population grows, the zone of fallow land shrinks. Slash-and-burn is terribly wasteful of land, since at least ten acres must lie fallow for each one that is being cultivated. It becomes necessary to return to a fallow field every five years instead of every ten or fifteen. There is no chance for the soil to replenish itself through rest. Each time a plot is farmed, more nutrients are taken out than are replaced. The land becomes a little less fertile each time it is used. A time comes when the entire vicinity has been exhausted, its soil destroyed by heat and rain.

In Africa today, great stretches of forest have been ruined in just this way. Basic changes in the environment have occurred: the temperature is now much higher, the humidity is much lower, and the soil is furrowed by erosion. It may be hundreds of years before the land is useful again.

When the rain forest is cleared away, then, a subtle balance is destroyed and fertility leaves the soil. In any farming area, not only in the tropics, the replacement of forest by crops will tend to drain the earth of its life-giving substances. In Europe and the United States, this problem was once met by letting the land lie fallow a few seasons, or by planting different crops in different years on the same soil. Today, chemical fertilizers are added to the soil to restore its vitality.

If fertilizers were used in the tropics, many of the problems of rain-forest agriculture would vanish. But fertilizers are expensive, and forest folk have no money. Most of them produce only enough to feed themselves and have nothing to sell for cash. So even where the existence of such things as fertilizers is known, it is impossible to obtain them. The absence of roads in the rain forests would make transportation of these chemicals to jungle villages extremely hard, in any event.

Since tremendous obstacles stand in the way of carrying on

farming in the jungles of Brazil as it is done in Kansas, other ways have been found to make use of forest land for agriculture.

The secret lies in maintaining forest conditions wherever possible. If a complete clearing is made, so that the soil is laid bare, the rainfall will leach minerals from the upper levels and the tropical sun will burn the ground to sterility. Some cover must always be left.

Bananas, one of the most successful of tropical crops, benefit from an upside-down kind of slash-and-burn cultivation, minus the burning. They must have plenty of sunshine as they grow, but they must also have a fertile soil. So banana rhizomes are planted in uncleared forest patches, and *then* the trees are felled. The slashed-down debris is allowed to remain on the field without being burned. The action of bacteria, termites, and fungi rots the dead logs and enriches the ground. The young banana plants grow up through this tangle of rotting matter. After each plant has borne its stem of fruit, it is cut down and left to decay, so that it will return its nutrients to the soil. At no time is the bare earth exposed to harm.

Rubber and coffee are also produced most successfully under semi-wild conditions. When Europeans first tried to develop rubber plantations in the tropics, they made the mistake of clearing the land of wild trees, terracing it, and neatly removing all undergrowth. This was costly and also pointless, for it swiftly led to soil depletion. *Hevea,* the South American rubber tree, is common in the wild state and does best when it is allowed to grow under forest conditions. Cacao is another important tree that must have a forestlike environment.

When attempts are made to grow tropical crops in the tidy fashion of temperate-zone farmers, they are doomed in advance. Sometimes huge plantations have had to be abandoned just like the tiny slash-and-burn plots of peasants, simply because the soil was not properly protected from leaching.

In the Congo, when it was under Belgian control, a fifty-thou-sand-acre experimental farm was maintained by scientists trying to find new ways of carrying on jungle agriculture. Because of the size of the Congo jungle and the almost total absence of roads, railway lines, and navigable waterways, it was considered impossible to transport chemical fertilizers to the interior. There-fore, some way of improving the traditional slash-and-burn methods had to be found.

The Belgian scientists knew that it was important to keep the soil continuously covered with vegetation. They worked out a rotation scheme that would protect the soil while yielding the maximum of useful crops. Peasant farmers were taught to plant rice and corn on partly cleared plots, then peanuts, cotton, cas-sava (an edible root highly important in tropical countries), and bananas, all in succession on the same field. At all times the

A banana plantation

ground was protected from scorching sun and beating rain, and dead plants of each crop provided fertility for the next.

Such advanced methods have been slow in reaching other countries, particularly those of Asia. There, rice has come to be the one and only crop. Rice is adapted to wet soils, and even on very poor soils will always produce something to eat. Where expanding populations cry out for food and the unwise clearing of the forest has made it difficult to grow other crops, rice is the easiest solution.

The tropics are lands of paradox. Hundreds of millions of people live in an idyllic Eden of great beauty, where winter never comes and flowers bloom all the year round. Yet in this realm of such seeming blessings, they can produce barely enough food to keep themselves alive.

The rain forest has other uses for man besides its agricultural potential. It is rich with valuable timber. Its soil contains fungi that have medicinal properties. (Such drugs as Aureomycin and streptomycin are made from tropical fungi.) It contains other useful plants. But until the people of the tropics have learned to defeat famine, commercial development of the forest resources must be postponed.

Today, in some parts of the world, men are slowly learning how to make use of the great promise of the rain forest. In other lands, the old mistakes are being repeated; the forest is being hacked blindly to destruction, and wind and rain and heat are allowed to do their deadly work.

But in millions of acres in a global belt along the equator, the rain forest is as it always has been. Man has not yet been able to put his mark on it.

Here are the giant trees, rising from buttressed bases, their crowns enmeshed with a fantastic tangle of lianas. Here are the low trees of the undergrowth, their smooth green leaves glistening with recent rain. Here are the epiphytes, sprouting like jagged-edged bouquets from the branches of the trees.

Through these dark groves flit the glass-winged butterflies. In that lofty canopy race the chattering monkeys. Within the damp ground, toiling termites perform their age-old tasks. The sun does not seem to be part of this world; only an occasional dancing yellow shaft reminds us of its existence. We hear the pattering of distant raindrops, striking the tops of the trees and bouncing from leaf to leaf, running along branches and vine-covered trunks, sluicing toward the cool earth. We feel the clammy mists of a place that has never known dryness.

We are strangers here in the timeless rain forest. It looks the way it looked a million years ago, when man was just another naked beast. We walk through it cautiously, warily, like the outsiders we are. We may think we know the rain forest, because we can describe the pattern of its canopies and give names to its inhabitants, but we do not really know this dark, secret place at all. This is the world of the rain forest: a silent world, a warm world, a green world, a wet world. Even at a time when mankind is reaching for the stars, it remains a place of mystery and wonder.

Bibliography

The books in the first group below will provide more information about the tropical rain forest and its creatures. Those marked with asterisks have outstanding illustrations or are otherwise of special value to young readers.

Bates, Marston, *Where Winter Never Comes*. New York, Charles Scribner's Sons, 1952. Informal and informative general survey of the tropics.

* Buchsbaum, Ralph, *Animals Without Backbones*, rev. ed. Chicago, University of Chicago Press, 1948. Outstanding treatment of insects, worms, and other lower organisms.

Collins, W. B., *The Perpetual Forest*. Philadelphia and New York, J. B. Lippincott Co., 1959. Accent on the African jungle.

Cutright, Paul Russell, *The Great Naturalists Explore South America*. New York, The Macmillan Company, 1940.

* Hargreaves, Dorothy and Bob, *Tropical Trees*. Portland, Oregon, Hargreaves Industrial, 1965. Excellent color photos of South and Central American trees in flower.

* McCormick, Jack, *The Living Forest*. New York, Harper & Row, 1959. Primarily about northern forests but useful for its fine illustrations and its good discussion of forest development.

161

* Sanderson, Ivan, *Ivan Sanderson's Book of Great Jungles.* New York, Julian Messner, Inc., 1965. Rambling but all-inclusive, with many photographs.

* Silverberg, Robert, *Forgotten by Time: A Book of Living Fossils.* New York, Thomas Y. Crowell Company, 1966. Accounts of sloths, anteaters, pangolins, and other forest creatures, with many illustrations.

* —— *Lost Cities and Vanished Civilizations.* Philadelphia, Chilton Books, 1962. Paperback reprint, Bantam Books, 1963. More information on Angkor and the Mayas.

TECHNICAL BOOKS AND OTHER SOURCES

Crist, Raymond, "Tropical Subsistence Agriculture in Latin America." Smithsonian Institution Annual Report. Washington, Government Printing Office, 1963.

Hahn, Emily, *Raffles of Singapore.* New York, Doubleday & Company, Inc., 1946.

Humboldt, Alexander von, *Personal Narrative of Travels to the Equinoctial Regions of America.* London, Henry G. Bohn, 1852.

Hylander, Clarence J., *The World of Plant Life.* New York, The Macmillan Company, 1944.

Kellner, L., *Alexander von Humboldt.* London, Oxford University Press, 1963.

Meggers, Betty J., and Evans, Clifford, *Archeological Investigations at the Mouth of the Amazon.* Washington, Government Printing Office, 1957.

Miller, Leo E., *In the Wilds of South America.* New York, Charles Scribner's Sons, 1919.

Oviedo, Gonzalo Fernández de, *Natural History of the West Indies.* Trans. and ed. by Sterling A. Stoudemire. Chapel Hill, The University of North Carolina Press, 1959.

Pendleton, Robert L., "The Place of Tropical Soils in Feeding the World." Smithsonian Institution Annual Report. Washington, Government Printing Office, 1955.

Ravenstein, E. G. *The Strange Adventures of Andrew Battell.* London, The Hakluyt Society, 1901.

Richards, P. W., *The Tropical Rain Forest*. Cambridge, England, Cambridge University Press, 1952.

Schiffers, Heinrich, *The Quest for Africa: Two Thousand Years of Exploration*. New York, G. P. Putnam's Sons, 1958.

Schneirla, T. C., "The Army Ants." Smithsonian Institution Annual Report. Washington, Government Printing Office, 1955.

Stanley, Henry M., *In Darkest Africa*. New York, Charles Scribner's Sons, 1890.

Waterton, Charles, *Wanderings in South America*. London, B. Fellowes, 1828.

Yule, Sir Henry, ed., *The Book of Ser Marco Polo*, 3d ed. rev. by Henri Cordier. London, John Murray, 1929.

MAGAZINE ARTICLES

Argo, Virgil N., "Strangler Fig, Native Epiphyte." *Natural History*, November, 1964.

Beebe, William, "The High World of the Rain Forest." *National Geographic Magazine*, June, 1958.

Fairchild, David, "The Jungles of Panama." *National Geographic Magazine*, February, 1922.

Harris, Jennie E., "Where Chocolate Comes From." *Natural History*, April, 1953.

Hingston, Maj. R.W.G., "A New World to Explore." *National Geographic Magazine*, November, 1932.

Lothrop, Eleanor, "The Banana—from Ground to Grocer." *Natural History*, November, 1956.

McNeil, Mary, "Lateritic Soils." *Scientific American*, November, 1964.

Pallister, John C., "Ghost Children of the Tropics." *Natural History*, November, 1956.

Stevens, Capt. Albert W., "Exploring the Valley of the Amazon in a Hydroplane." *National Geographic Magazine*, April, 1926.

Zahl, Paul A., "Giant Insects of the Amazon." *National Geographic Magazine*, May, 1959.

———— "In the Gardens of Olympus." *National Geographic Magazine*, July, 1955.

Index

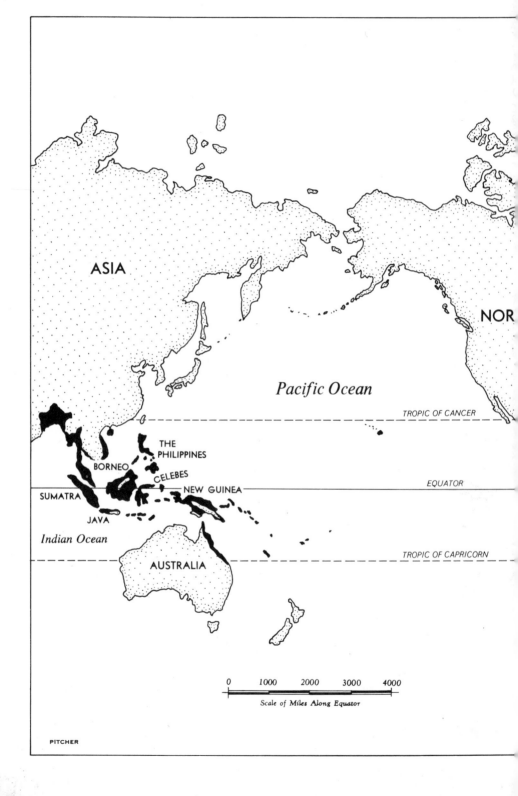

ASIA

NOR

Pacific Ocean

TROPIC OF CANCER

THE
PHILIPPINES

BORNEO

CELEBES

NEW GUINEA

EQUATOR

SUMATRA

JAVA

Indian Ocean

TROPIC OF CAPRICORN

AUSTRALIA

0   1000   2000   3000   4000

Scale of Miles Along Equator

PITCHER